MSCHOLASTIC

Kindergarten

Jumbo Workbook

This book belongs to

_____

Cover design by Sequel Creative
Cover art by Patrick Girouard
Interior illustrations by Janet Armbrust, Jane Dippold, Rusty Fletcher,
James Graham Hale, Kathy Marlin, Sherry Neidigh, and Karen Sevaly.

ISBN 978-0-545-64890-5

11 12 13 14 15 16 17 18   08   23 22 21 20 19 18 17 16

Dear Parents,

The power to succeed is in every child! The question is: How can you help your child achieve this success and become an independent, lifelong learner?

You have already taken the first step! This *Kindergarten Jumbo Workbook* is the perfect way to support the learning your child needs to be successful in school.

Research shows that independent practice helps children gain mastery of essential skills. This book includes carefully selected, teacher-tested activities that give kindergartners exactly the practice they need. Topics covered include:

- Alphabet and Phonics
- Sight Words
- Handwriting
- Number Recognition and Counting
- Addition
- Thinking Skills

You'll also find assessments to help you keep track of your child's progress—and provide important practice with standardized test formats.

Let's get started! Your involvement will make this a valuable educational experience and will support and enhance your child's learning.

Enjoy!

Hindie

Hindie Weissman
Educational Consultant,
27+ years teaching experience

Learn and Succeed

Welcome!

Kindergarten is a critical stepping stone on the road to learning success! This workbook has been carefully designed to help ensure your child has the tools he or she needs to soar in school. On the 300-plus pages that follow, you'll find plenty of practice in each of these must-know curriculum areas:

ALPHABET & PHONICS	READING READINESS	WORD BUILDING	EARLY CONCEPTS
• Identifying Letters • Sequencing Letters • Writing Letters • Identifying Vowels, Consonants, and Blends • Recognizing Word Families	• Sequencing Stories • Recognizing Similarities and Differences • Identifying Cause and Effect	• Mastering Sight Words • Mastering Position Words • Mastering Science and Social Studies Words	• Identifying Opposites • Comparing Sizes • Sorting and Classifying

NUMBERS	MATH CONCEPTS	FOLLOWING DIRECTIONS	THINKING SKILLS
• Identifying Numbers • Counting • Writing Numbers • Adding	• Identifying Shapes • Understanding Patterns • Using Pictures to Solve Problems	• Building Listening Skills • Performing Steps in Sequence • Taking Bubble Tests	• Identifying Sets • Recognizing Relationships • Simple Reasoning

Helping your child build essential skills is easy!

These teacher-approved activities have been specially developed to make learning both accessible and enjoyable. On each page, you'll find:

Directions
The read-aloud directions are easy for your child to understand.

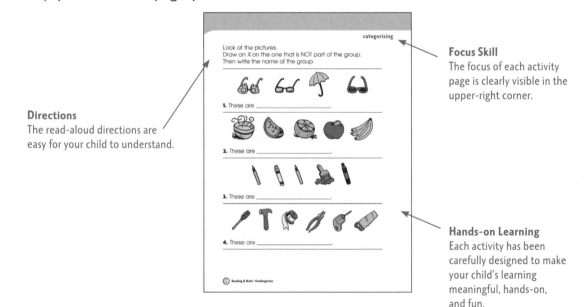

Focus Skill
The focus of each activity page is clearly visible in the upper-right corner.

Hands-on Learning
Each activity has been carefully designed to make your child's learning meaningful, hands-on, and fun.

with Scholastic!

These great extras are guaranteed to make learning extra engaging!

This workbook is loaded with lots of motivating, special components including:

SPECIAL ACTIVITIES TO GET READY FOR FIRST GRADE▶

Give your child a head start in first grade with this BONUS assortment of get-ready activities.

◀CONNECTION TO ONLINE LEARNING

Boost computer literacy with this special link to a treasury of skill-building online activities at www.scholastic.com/success.

MOTIVATING STICKERS▶

Mark the milestones of your child's learning path with these bright, kid-pleasing stickers.

◀INSTANT FLASH CARDS

Promote reading fluency with these fun flash cards.

REWARD CERTIFICATE▶

Celebrate your child's leap in learning with this colorful, pull-out completion certificate.

◀LIST OF THE BEST BOOKS FOR YOUNG LEARNERS

Reinforce key concepts and build a love of reading with this great list of learning-rich books selected by top educators. See page 12.

QUICK ASSESSMENT TESTS ▶

Make sure your child *really* masters each must-know skill with the instant assessment tests that conclude each section.

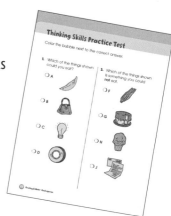

Table of Contents

Scholastic

Scholastic

Scholastic

Tips for Success

Here are some tips to help your child get the most out of this workbook:

- Provide a quiet, comfortable place for your child to work.

- Make sure your child understands the directions.

- Encourage your child to use colorful pencils and markers to make learning fun.

- Check completed work as soon as possible and review corrected work with your child.

- Pay attention to areas where your child is having difficulty. Spend extra time to help him or her master those skills.

- Provide a special area at home where your child's work can be displayed.

- Be positive and encouraging. Praise your child for his or her efforts and good work.

Scholastic

Read with Your Child

Reading to your child and having him or her read to you is an extremely effective way of supporting your child's learning. When you read with him or her, make sure your child is actively participating. Here are five ways to support your child's reading:

1. Let your child choose the book.

2. Look at the cover of the book and ask your child what he or she thinks the story will be about.

3. As you read the book, locate a good stopping point and ask your child to predict what will happen next. Then read to confirm the prediction or correct it.

4. Discuss the characters in the story: Are they kind? good? bad? clever? Are they like characters in another book?

5. When you finish the story, have your child retell it.

Read with Your Child

Looking for a great book to read to your child? Here are some top teacher picks:

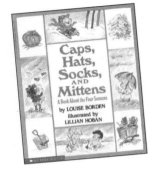

- *Brown Bear, Brown Bear, What Do You See?* by Bill Martin, Jr. (Henry Holt, 1966).

- *Caps, Hats, Socks, and Mittens* by Louise Borden (Scholastic, 1989).

- *Click, Clack, Moo: Cows That Type* by Doreen Cronin (Simon & Schuster, 2000).

- *Hey! Get Off Our Train* by John Burningham (Crown Publishing, 1989).

- *How Giraffe Got Such a Long Neck. . . and Why Rhino Is So Grumpy* by Michael Rosen (Penguin, 1993).

- *If You Give a Mouse a Cookie* by Laura Joffe Numeroff (Laura Geringer, 1985).

- *My Painted House, My Friendly Chicken, and Me* by Maya Angelou (Random House Children's Books, 2003).

- *Of Colors and Things* by Tana Hoban (HarperTrophy, 1996).

- *Planting a Rainbow* by Lois Ehlert (Harcourt Brace Jovanovich, 1988).

- *A Pocket for Corduroy* by Don Freeman (Puffin Books, 1978).

The Alphabet/Manuscript Handwriting

"Look, mom, I can write the alphabet!" What a delightful thing to hear your child say. In this section, your child will practice writing upper- and lowercase letters of the alphabet.

What to Do

Have your child use a pencil to trace and then write each letter. Next, help your child identify and write words that start with that letter. He or she might choose words from the word and picture cards.

Invite your child to color the pictures. Review the flash cards frequently to help your child develop his or her vocabulary skills during the year.

Keep On Going!

• As you drive or walk with your child, point out signs around the neighborhood. Have your child identify the letters in the signs. Then together, say the words.

• While reading a magazine or the newspaper, encourage your child to look for words that begin with a particular letter, such as *B,* on the page and circle them.

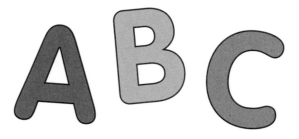

I am learning about the letter A a.
This is how I write it:

Here are some words that start with the letter A a:

This is my picture of an _____ .

Scholastic

Say the words. Color the pictures.

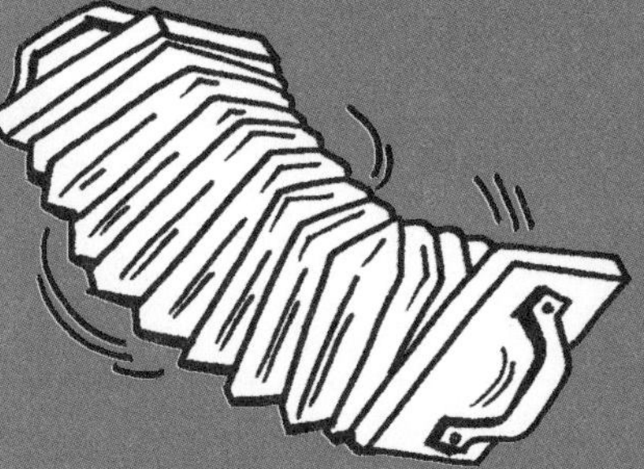

accordion	astronaut	ax
anchor	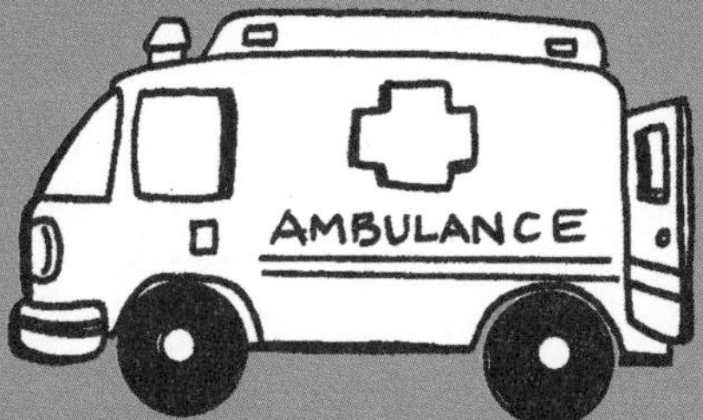 ambulance	acorn
aardvark	ape	apple

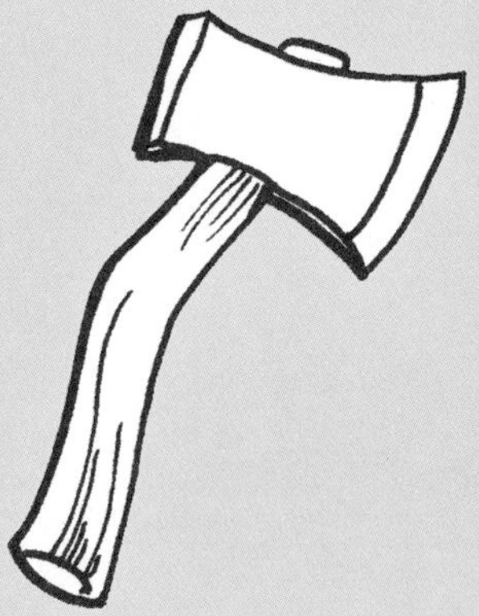

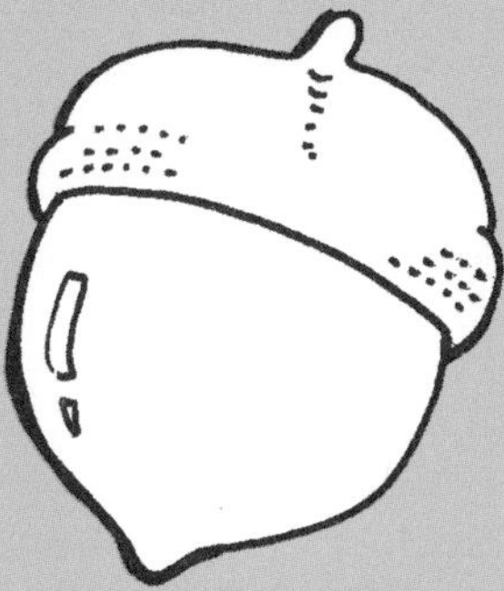

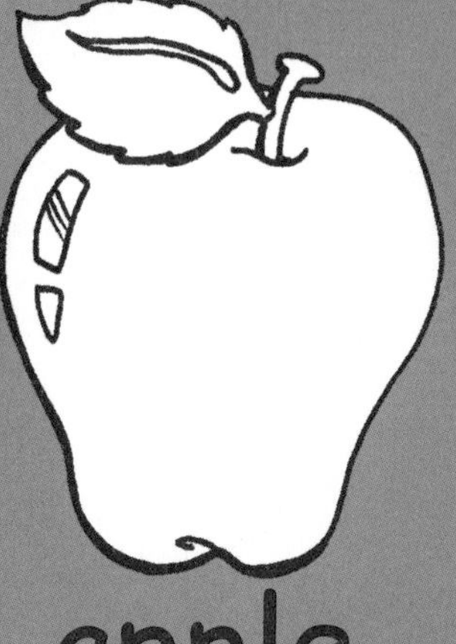

Scholastic

I am learning about the letter B b.
This is how I write it:

B B

b b

Here are some words that start with the letter B b:

_____   _____

--------------------------------   --------------------------------

_____   _____

--------------------------------   --------------------------------

_____   _____

This is my picture of a _____ .

Scholastic

Say the words. Color the pictures.

balloon

ball

boat

bicycle

bed

book

baby

butterfly

bird

Scholastic

I am learning about the letter C c.
This is how I write it:

Here are some words that start with the letter C c:

This is my picture of a _____ .

Scholastic

Say the words. Color the pictures.

crab

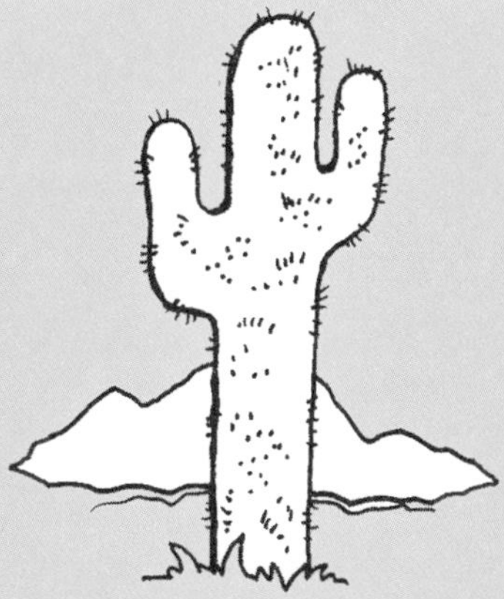

cactus

cake

calendar

car

caterpillar

cone

cup

corn

I am learning about the letter D d.
This is how I write it:

D D

d d

Here are some words that start with the letter D d:

_____   _____

- - - - - - - - - - - -   - - - - - - - - - - - -

_____   _____

_____   _____

- - - - - - - - - - - -   - - - - - - - - - - - -

_____   _____

This is my picture of a _____ .

Scholastic

Say the words. Color the pictures.

dolphin

dinosaur

dice

dollar

doll

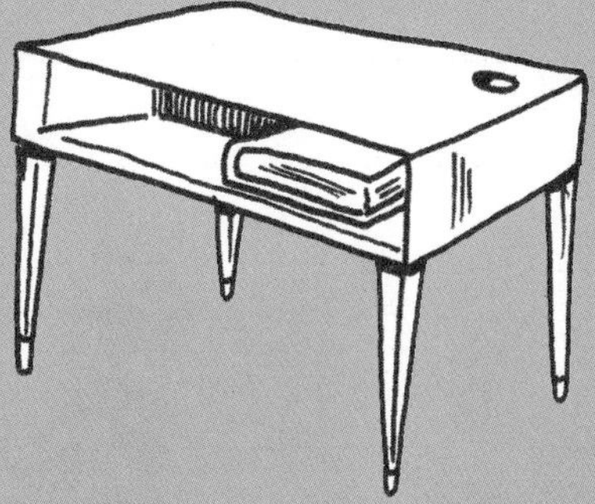

desk

door

duck

dog

I am learning about the letter E e.
This is how I write it:

Here are some words that start with the letter E e:

This is my picture of an _____ .

Say the words. Color the pictures.

elephant	eagle	earth
elf	egg	eight
eye	ear	 exit sign

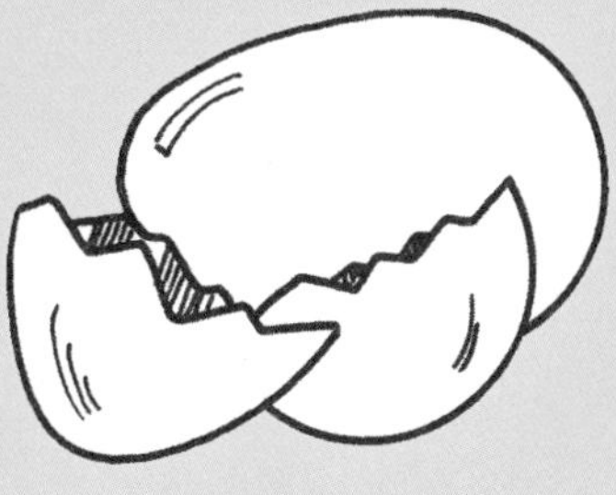

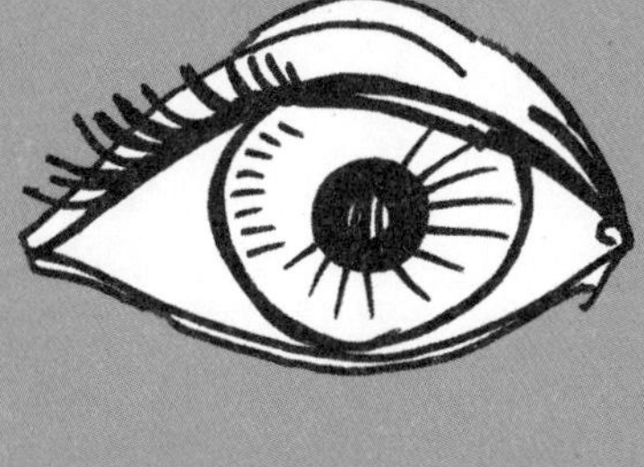

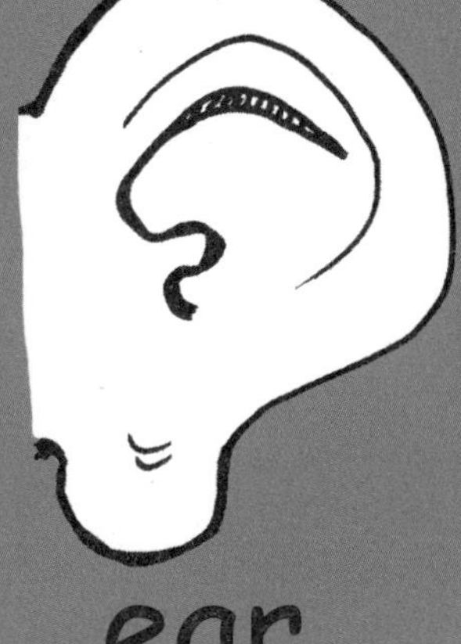

I am learning about the letter F f.
This is how I write it:

Here are some words that start with the letter F f:

This is my picture of a _____ .

Say the words. Color the pictures.

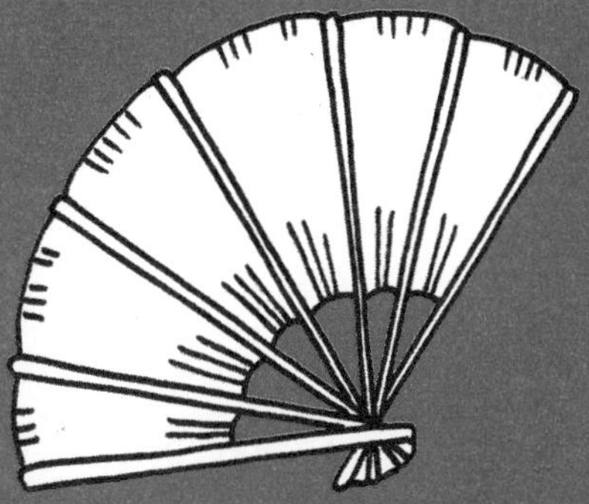

fan

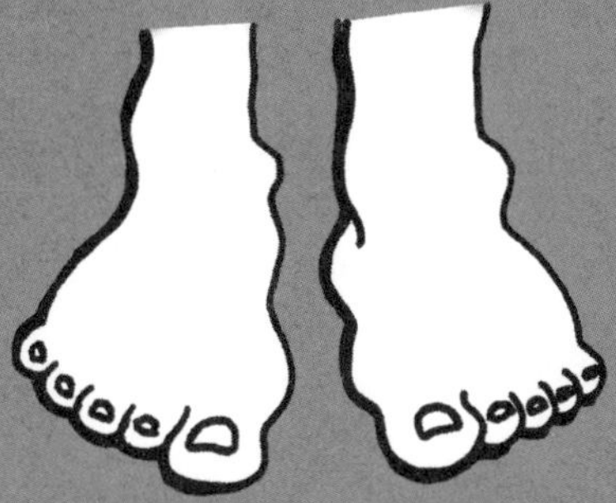

feet

fox

finger

five

feather

fish

fire

fork

I am learning about the letter G g.
This is how I write it:

Here are some words that start with the letter G g:

This is my picture of a _____ .

Scholastic

Say the words. Color the pictures.

game	gate	gift
giraffe	girl	goose
gum	goat	guitar

Scholastic

I am learning about the letter H h.
This is how I write it:

Here are some words that start with the letter H h:

This is my picture of a _____ .

Scholastic

Say the words. Color the pictures.

heart

hammer

hamburger

hen

hand

house

hose

horn

hat

I am learning about the letter I i.
This is how I write it:

Here are some words that start with the letter I i:

This is my picture of an _____ .

Say the words. Color the pictures.

Scholastic

I am learning about the letter J j.
This is how I write it:

Here are some words that start with the letter J j:

This is my picture of a _____ .

Say the words. Color the pictures.

I am learning about the letter K k.
This is how I write it:

Here are some words that start with the letter K k:

This is my picture of a _____ .

Say the words. Color the pictures.

kangaroo kettle keys

king kite kick

kitten ketchup kitchen

Scholastic

I am learning about the letter L l.
This is how I write it:

Here are some words that start with the letter L l:

This is my picture of a _____ .

Scholastic

Say the words. Color the pictures.

log	lemons	ladder
ladybugs	lamp	lobster
lizard	letter	lion

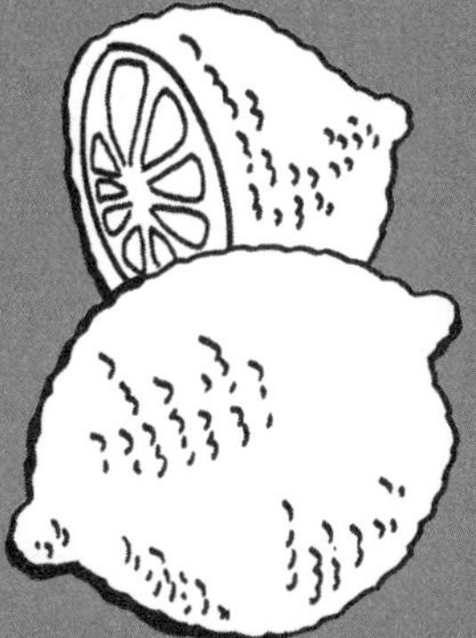

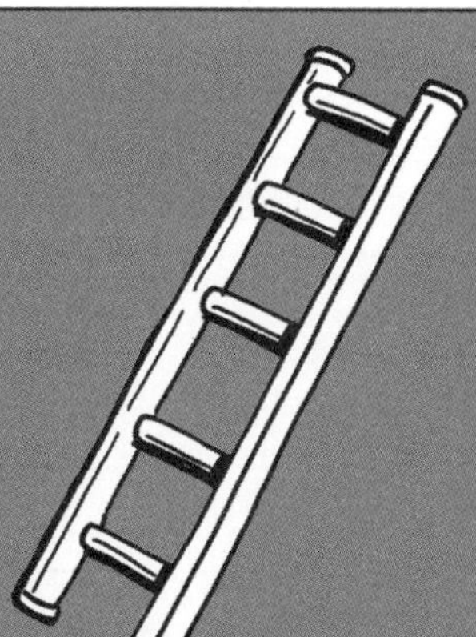

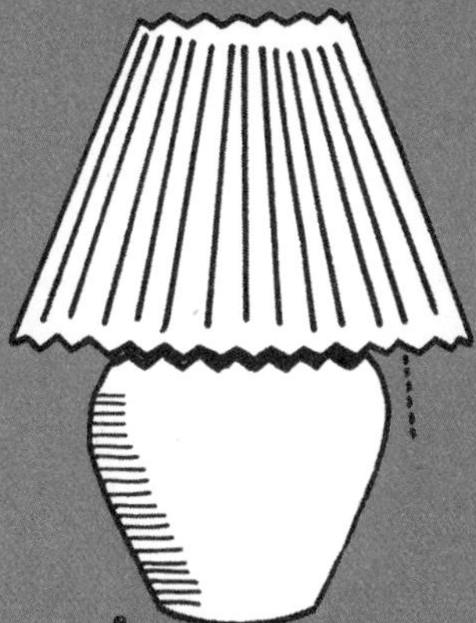

I am learning about the letter M m.
This is how I write it:

M M

m m

Here are some words that start with the letter M m:

This is my picture of a _____ .

Scholastic

Say the words. Color the pictures.

mailbox	mask	mushroom
mittens	muffin	mouse
money	monkey	mirror

Scholastic

I am learning about the letter N n.
This is how I write it:

N N N

n n n

Here are some words that start with the letter N n:

This is my picture of a _____ .

Say the words. Color the pictures.

nest

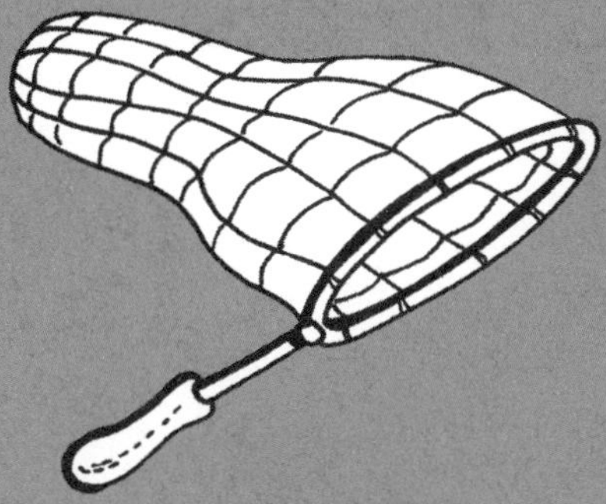

net

necklace

nickel

newspaper

nail

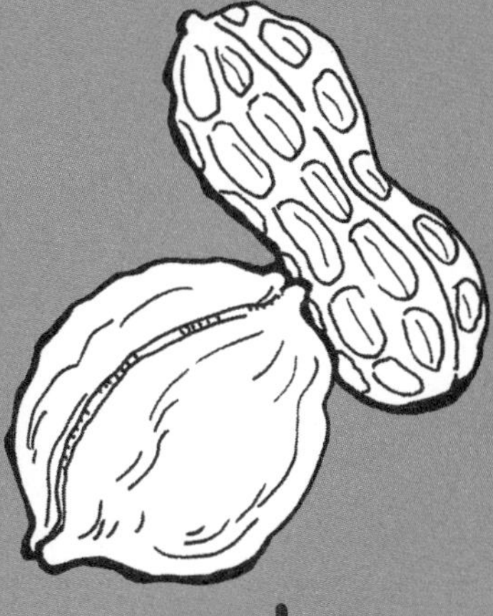

nuts

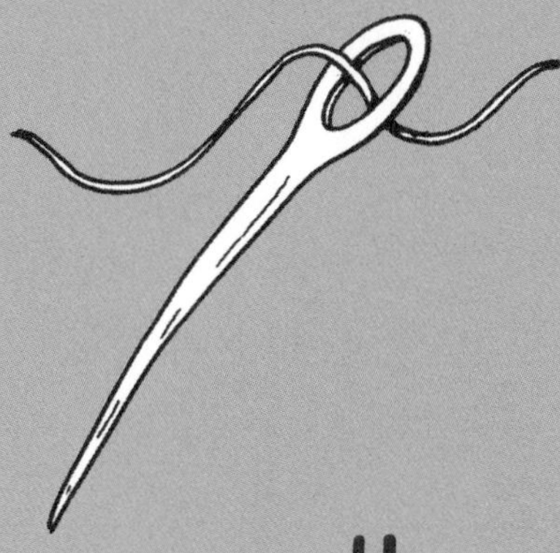

needle

nine

I am learning about the letter O o.
This is how I write it:

Here are some words that start with the letter O o:

This is my picture of an _____ .

Say the words. Color the pictures.

octopus

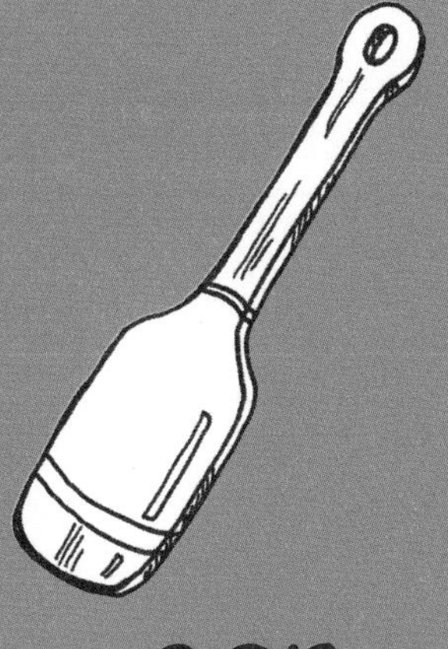

oar

ostrich

owl

oil can

orange juice

ornament

onions

oatmeal

I am learning about the letter P p.
This is how I write it:

P P

p p

Here are some words that start with the letter P p:

This is my picture of a _____ .

Scholastic

Say the words. Color the pictures.

Scholastic

I am learning about the letter Q q.
This is how I write it:

Here are some words that start with the letter Q q:

This is my picture of a _____ .

Scholastic

Say the words. Color the pictures.

question mark

quilt

quarter

queen

quart

quacking

I am learning about the letter R r.
This is how I write it:

R R

r r

Here are some words that start with the letter R r:

This is my picture of a _____ .

Scholastic

Say the words. Color the pictures.

radio

rainbow

rabbit

rock

rocking horse

roller skate

rooster

rolling pin

refrigerator

I am learning about the letter S s.
This is how I write it:

S S

s s

Here are some words that start with the letter S s:

This is my picture of a _____ .

Scholastic

Say the words. Color the pictures.

sailboat	sandwich	sink
snowflake	seal	soap
seven	socks	six

I am learning about the letter T t.
This is how I write it:

Here are some words that start with the letter T t:

This is my picture of a _____ .

Say the words. Color the pictures.

table	top	tiger
television	toothbrush	telephone
toilet	turkey	turtle

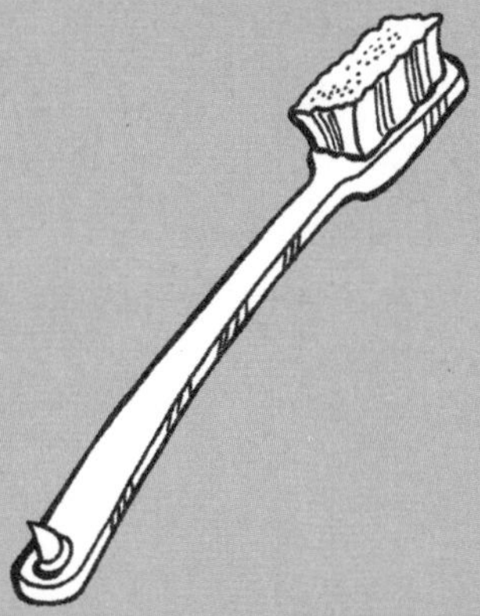

Scholastic

I am learning about the letter U u.
This is how I write it:

U U U

U U

Here are some words that start with the letter U u:

This is my picture of a/an _____ .

Scholastic

Say the words. Color the pictures.

ukulele

umbrella

umpire

unicorn

utensils

up

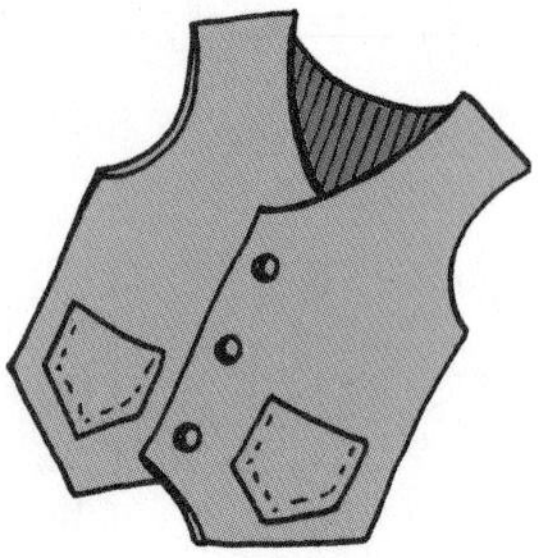

I am learning about the letter V v.
This is how I write it:

Here are some words that start with the letter V v:

This is my picture of a _____ .

Say the words. Color the pictures.

vacuum

van

vase

vegetables

vest

violin

volcano

valentine

video cassette

Scholastic

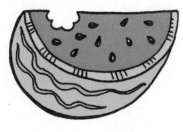

I am learning about the letter W w.
This is how I write it:

W W W

w w

Here are some words that start with the letter W w:

This is my picture of a _____ .

Say the words. Color the pictures.

worm

watermelon

wishing well

walrus

web

watch

window

wagon

windmill

Scholastic

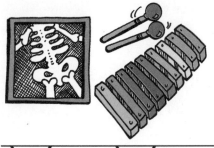

I am learning about the letter X x.
This is how I write it:

X   X
X   X

Here are some words that start with the letter X x:

This is my picture of a/an _____ .

Scholastic

I am learning about the letter Y y.
This is how I write it:

Here are some words that start with the letter Y y:

This is my picture of a _____ .

I am learning about the letter Z z.
This is how I write it:

Here are some words that start with the letter Z z:

This is my picture of a _____ .

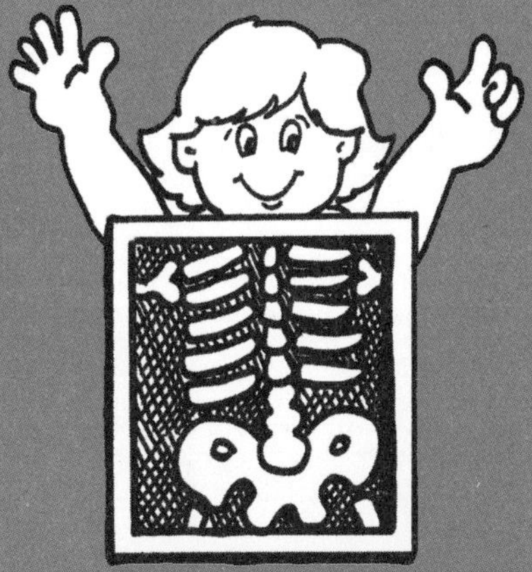

x-ray

xylophone

yawn

yield sign

yo-yo

yarn

zebra

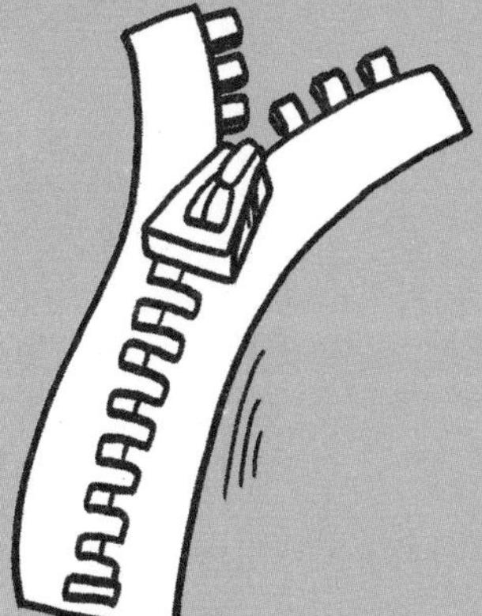

zipper

zero

Scholastic

Alphabet Practice Test

Choose the letter that comes next. Color in the bubble next to that letter.

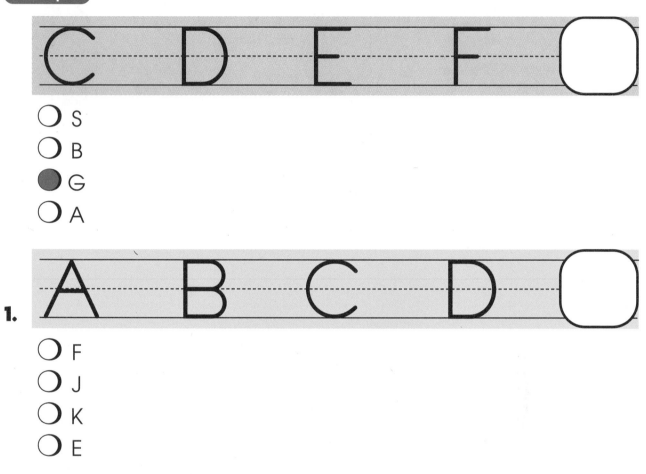

Example

C   D   E   F   ◯

○ S
● G
○ B
○ A

1.

A   B   C   D   ◯

○ F
○ J
○ K
○ E

2.

K   L   M   N   ◯

○ A
○ Z
○ O
○ P

Scholastic

Alphabet Practice Test

Choose the letter that comes next. Color in the bubble next to that letter.

3.

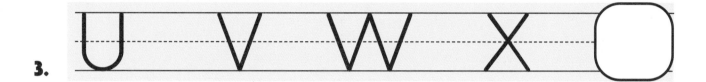

○ Y

○ Z

○ Q

○ N

4.

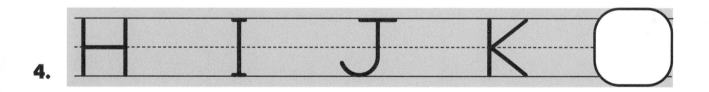

○ N

○ C

○ L

○ M

Alphabet Practice Test

Choose the letter that comes next. Color in the bubble next to that letter.

5.

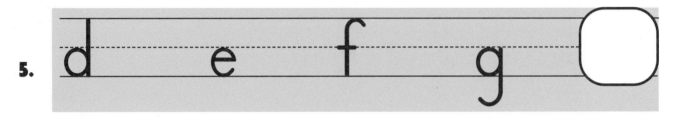

d   e   f   g

○ i

○ h

○ b

○ k

6.

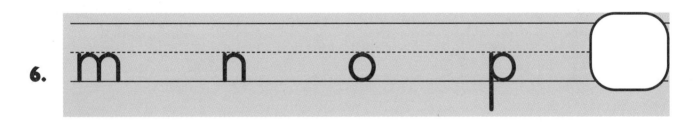

m   n   o   p

○ w

○ c

○ l

○ q

Scholastic

Alphabet Practice Test

Choose the letter that comes next. Color in the bubble next to that letter.

7.

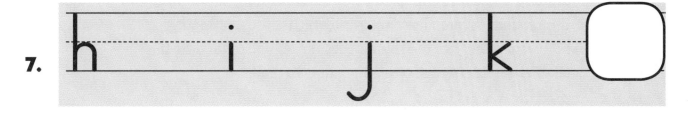

- ○ a
- ○ b
- ○ l
- ○ m

8.

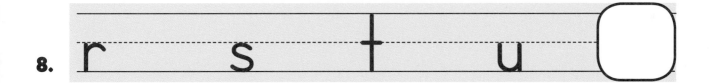

- ○ w
- ○ h
- ○ j
- ○ v

Scholastic

Phonics

"I know the sounds these letters make!" When you hear your child say that, you can rest assured he or she is building phonics skills. In this section, children learn phonics, which is the relationship between letters and the sounds they make. Understanding this relationship is essential to learning how to read.

What to Do

The activity pages in this section will give your child practice in identifying vowels and consonants, beginning and ending sounds in words, short- and long-vowel sounds and spellings, and consonant blends.

Have your child complete each activity page, and then review it together. On some pages you will see a light bulb. Spend time discussing the answers to these questions.

Keep On Going!

• Point to objects around the house. Have your child identify the beginning or ending sounds and letters of the objects. Then have your child point to objects as you identify long- and short-vowel sounds. Take turns identifying the various letter-sound relationships.

• Create riddles with your child to practice beginning or ending consonant sounds. For example, "It's round and fun to play with. It ends with the *l* sound." (ball)

There are 26 letters in the alphabet. Five of the letters are vowels: **A, E, I, O,** and **U.**

All the rest are consonants.

Look at the alphabet below. Mark an **X** through the five vowels: **A, E, I, O,** and **U.**

Now say the names of all the consonants.

A B C D E F G H I

J K L M N O P Q

R S T U V W X Y Z

How many consonants are there? _____
Color each balloon that has a consonant in it.

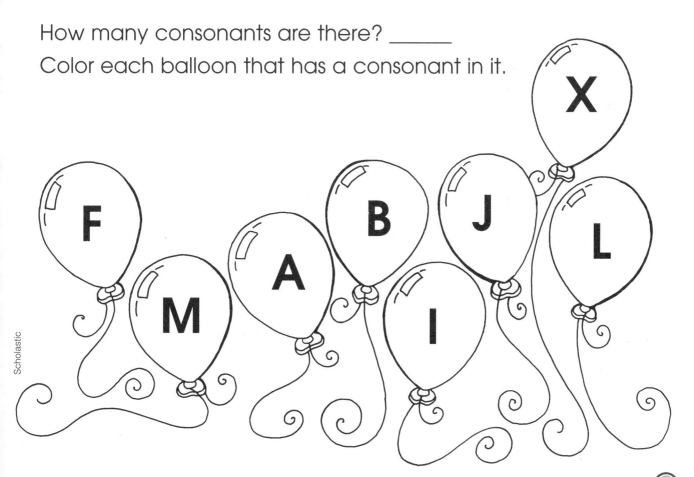

Scholastic

B *makes the sound you hear at the beginning of the words*
Bobby *and* **bear.**

Help Bobby the bear find ten things
in this store that begin with **b**.
Draw a circle around each one.

 What insect buzzes around flowers and makes honey?

D *makes the sound you hear at the beginning of the words* **doctor** *and* **Dave**.

Look in Doctor Dave's bag. Color only the pictures that begin with **d**. Put an **X** on the pictures that do not begin with **d**.

 She is another kind of doctor. She works on your teeth. Her job begins with *d*. Who is she?

Scholastic

Reading & Math · Kindergarten 71

F *makes the sound you hear at the beginning of the words* **fancy** *and* **fish**.

Draw a bubble around the pictures that begin with **f**. Put an **X** on the pictures that do not begin with **f**.

 This word begins with *f*. **It names a brave person who saves people if their houses are burning. Who is this person?**

L *makes the sound you hear at the beginning of the words* **lazy** *and* **lion**.

Help Lazy the lion find a word that begins with **l** to match each picture. Circle the correct word.

lamp clock	zipper lace	tree leaf	ladder hoe
ladybug bee	lake town	dog lamb	hand leg
lightning snow	apple lemon	book letter	lettuce corn
nose lips	lizard goat	worm lobster	log rock

This word begins with an *l*. It is a good feeling that you have about the people you like the most. It makes you want to hug someone! What is it?

Scholastic

M *makes the sound you hear at the beginning of the words* **Mike** *and* **mailman**.

Look at the mail below. Circle each piece of mail that begins with **m.** If the picture does not begin with **m**, put an **X** through it.

 I am a woman in your family. I take care of you. I love you. You call me a name that begins with *m*. Who am I?

Scholastic

 N *makes the sound you hear at the beginning of the words* **Nancy** *and* **nurse***.*

Color the lollipops below that have pictures beginning with **n**.

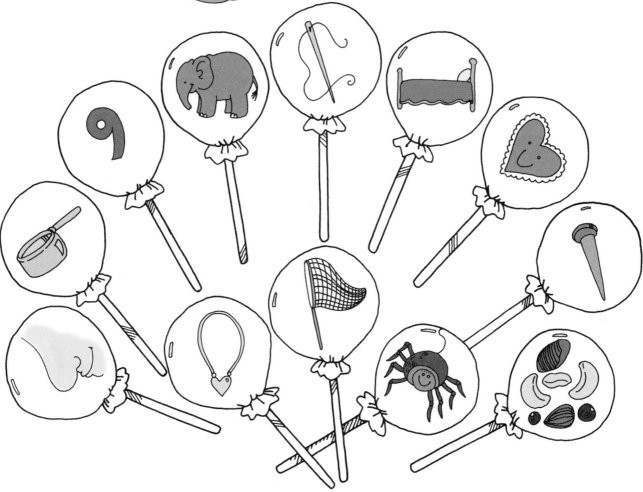

 This item begins with *n*. It is made of big sheets of paper. It has lots of pictures and words on it. It tells what is happening in the world. Grownups like to read it. What is it? Find one of these and look at one page of it. Find words you know. Circle them with a marker. Show a grownup what you can read!

Reading & Math • Kindergarten

P *makes the sound you hear at the beginning of the words* **Patsy** *and* **pig**.

Use a purple crayon to
write the letter **p** on top of each
picture below that begins with **p**.

 This item is a word that begins with *p*. **It has a head and a tail, but it is not an animal.
It is a copper-colored coin. What is it? Put one under this sheet of paper and rub over it
with a crayon.**

Scholastic

R *makes the sound you hear at the beginning of the words* **Ricky** *and* **rabbit**.

Circle the **r** word that tells what Ricky is doing in each picture.

rest play	swim run	ride hug
rock look	climb rake	stand roll
read sing	rope feed	rip talk
row eat	race walk	sleep rush

 This word begins with r. It blasts off into outer space. What is it?

S *makes the sound you hear at the beginning of the words* **silly** *and* **Sally**.

Color each space orange that has a picture in it that begins with **s**. If the picture does not begin with **s**, do not color that space.

 If you take two pieces of bread and put peanut butter on one and jelly on the other, then stick them together, what have you made? It begins with *s*.

T *makes the sound you hear at the beginning of the words* **Tammy** *and* **teacher**.

1. **Trace over the letter in each row.**
2. **Color the pictures in each row that begin with *t*.**

 This item begins with *t*. Campers sleep in it. What is it?

W *makes the sound you hear at the beginning of the words* **Willy** *and* **worm.**

In the story below, there are 11 words that begin with **w**. Draw a wiggly line under each one.

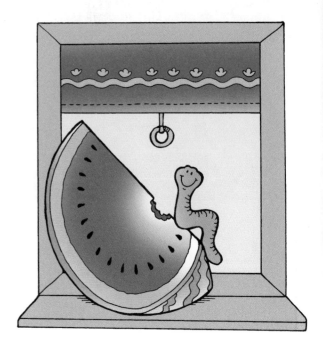

Willy the worm felt hungry. He wanted something to eat. He saw a watermelon in the window. He climbed up on the wagon. He wiggled up the wall. Then he took a bite. Wow! It was wonderful!

Now, circle each word that you underlined in the puzzle. The words go across and down.

x	w	i	g	g	l	e	d	v	t
w	a	t	e	r	m	e	l	o	n
o	g	e	k	p	r	s	b	y	w
w	o	r	m	h	f	l	x	z	i
k	n	c	w	i	n	d	o	w	l
g	v	w	a	n	t	e	d	a	l
u	w	h	s	r	z	q	g	l	y
w	o	n	d	e	r	f	u	l	a

 This begins with *w*. You cannot see it, but you can feel it. Sometimes you can hear it blowing. It makes the trees sway. What is it?

Scholastic

C *can make two sounds. If the vowels* **e** *or* **i** *come after the* **c***, then* **c** *will have the* **s** *sound. If one of the other vowels (***a***,* **o***,* **u***) comes after the* **c***, then* **c** *will have the* **k** *sound.*

Look at the pictures and words on this page. If a word begins with an *s* sound, as in *city*, circle **s**. If it begins with a *k* sound, as in *country*, circle **k**.

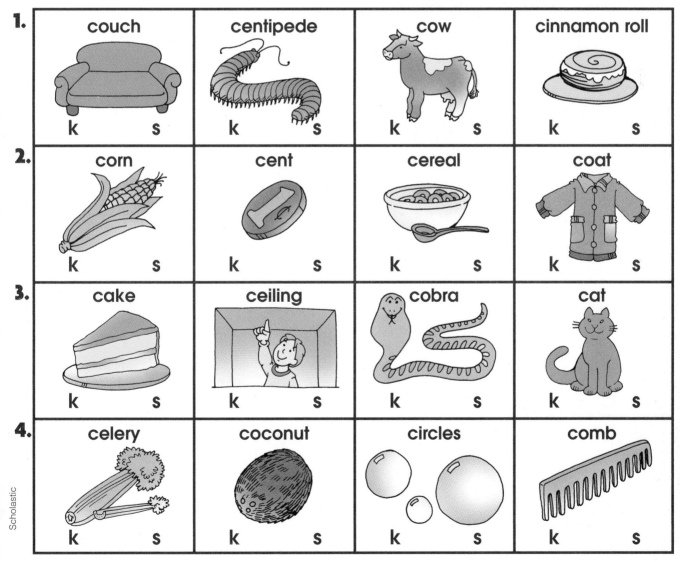

1. couch — k s
   centipede — k s
   cow — k s
   cinnamon roll — k s

2. corn — k s
   cent — k s
   cereal — k s
   coat — k s

3. cake — k s
   ceiling — k s
   cobra — k s
   cat — k s

4. celery — k s
   coconut — k s
   circles — k s
   comb — k s

*G can make two sounds. Usually, words that begin with g make the same sound that you hear in **Gary** and **goat**. But sometimes a g can sound like a j, as in **George** and **giraffe**. This usually happens when the vowels e or i come after the g, but not always. The best way to figure out which g sound to use is to try both sounds and see which one makes sense. For example, try saying goat with both g sounds. See? One of them does not make sense!*

Look at each picture below. If the picture begins like *goat*, circle **g**. If the picture begins like *giraffe*, circle **j**.

1.

gate	girl	gingerbread man	gift
g j	g j	g j	g j

2.

giant	guitar	gum	gerbil
g j	g j	g j	g j

3.

goose	gorilla	general	gymnast
g j	g j	g j	g j

Scholastic

To help you hear the ending sound, say the word and stretch out the last sound. For example, when you see the picture of the bear, say "bear-r-r-r-r."

Say the name of each animal. Write the ending sound in the box by its tail.

 This creature lives in the sea. It does not have a tail. It has eight arms. Its head looks like a balloon. It ends with *s*.

Scholastic

Help Larry Last find the last sound that each word makes. Circle the correct letter under each lunchbox.

1.

k   n   s   r   g   l   s   f   r

2.

   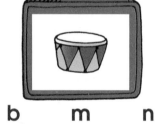   

n   d   z   b   m   n   t   k   p

3.

k   f   d   m   x   r   g   z   l

4.

d   v   r   l   k   d   g   t   f

You do this while you are asleep. It is like watching a movie in your head. It ends with *m*. What is it?

Scholastic

Find two words on each train that end with the same sound. Circle them. Then write the letter of the ending sound in the caboose.

Scholastic

It's time to raise the flags! Listen to the ending sound
of each picture name.

Color the **s** picture
flags **orange**.

Color the **l** picture
flags **purple**.

Color the **p** picture
flags **green**.

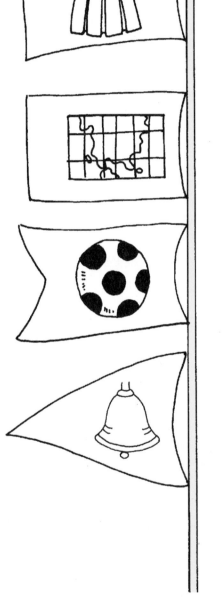
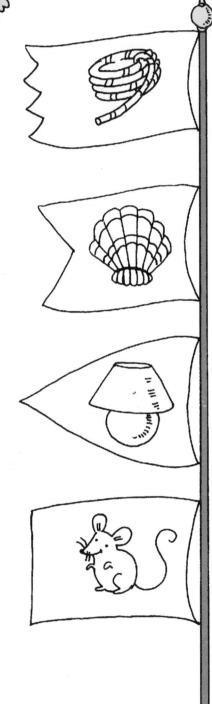

Scholastic

Read the letter in each row. Fill in the circle next to each
picture whose name **begins** with that sound.

1. p ○ ○ ○

2. n ○ ○ ○

3. q ○ ○ ○

4. d ○ ○ ○

5. f ○ ○ ○

Read the letter in each row. Fill in the circle next to each
picture whose name **ends** with that sound.

6. g ○ ○ ○

7. k ○ ○ ○

8. s ○ ○ ○

9. t ○ ○ ○

10. l ○ ○ ○

Scholastic

 There are 26 letters in the alphabet. Five of the letters are **vowels**. *They are* **a**, **e**, **i**, **o**, *and* **u**.

Look at the alphabet train.

Color the *a* car red.
Color the *e* car blue.
Color the *i* car orange.
Color the *o* car purple.
Color the *u* car green.

 Sometimes the letter **y** *can be a vowel.*

Color the *y* car yellow.

Look at each store sign. Circle each vowel you can find. There are 13 of them.

Dentist

Candy
Store

Bob's
Burgers

Flower
Shop

Bank

Scholastic

The **consonant-vowel-consonant rule:** *When only one vowel comes between consonants, that vowel is usually short.*

Unscramble the letters to spell each word. Circle the short vowel.

1. atr _____	**2.** aht _____	**3.** ktac _____
4. mkas _____	**5.** naf _____	**6.** plam _____
7. pca _____	**8.** dDa _____	**9.** tarp _____
10. dahn _____	**11.** palc _____	**12.** cklab _____

Scholastic

Reading & Math • Kindergarten 89

Short e *makes the sound you hear at the beginning of* **egg**. *To help you remember the short-*e *sound, stretch out the beginning of the word like this:* e-e-e-egg.

Help Ed find the eggs that have pictures with the short-*e* sound. Color these eggs brown. If the picture does not have the short-*e* sound, leave the egg white.

 When you say this word you nod your head up and down. It means the opposite of *no*. It has the short-*e* sound. What word is it?

Scholastic

Short i *makes the sound you hear at the beginning of* **igloo**. *To help you remember the short-*i* sound, stretch out the beginning of the word like this:* i-i-i-igloo.

Outline the pictures with the short-*i* sound in blue. If the picture does not have a short-*i* sound, draw an **X** on it.

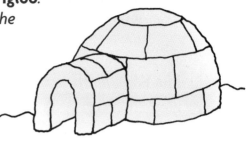

Scholastic

Short o *makes the sound you hear at the beginning of* **olive**. *To help you remember the short-*o *sound, stretch out the beginning of the word like this:* o-o-o-olive.

Help Oliver find the olives that have pictures with the short-*o* sound. Color these olives green. If the picture does not have the short-*o* sound, color the olive black.

Scholastic

The **consonant-vowel-consonant rule:** *When only one vowel comes between consonants, that vowel is usually short.*

Circle each word with the short-*u* sound. Then connect the words with the short-*u* sound to help Slug Bug find its way home.

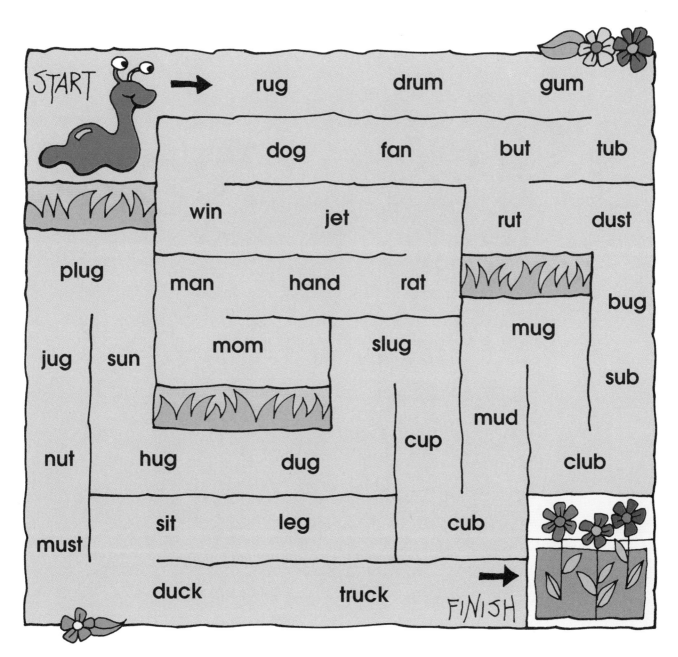

START → rug   drum   gum

dog   fan   but   tub

win   jet   rut   dust

plug   man   hand   rat   bug

mug

jug   sun   mom   slug   sub

mud

nut   hug   dug   cup   club

sit   leg   cub

must

duck   truck   FINISH

Circle the things in the picture that rhyme with **rat** .

hat

shirt

pants

trees

cat

mat

bat

 Name two things that rhyme with *rat* that are not in the picture.

Scholastic

Help Tad Frog find his way across the pond. Color the pictures green that rhyme with **pad** .

Help make the delivery. Follow the pictures that rhyme with **van** 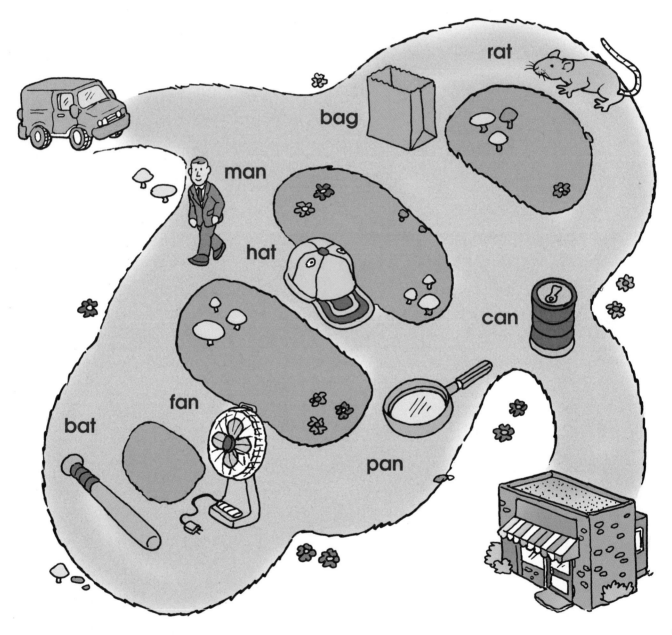.

Color the picture in each row that rhymes with the first picture.

1.  fan	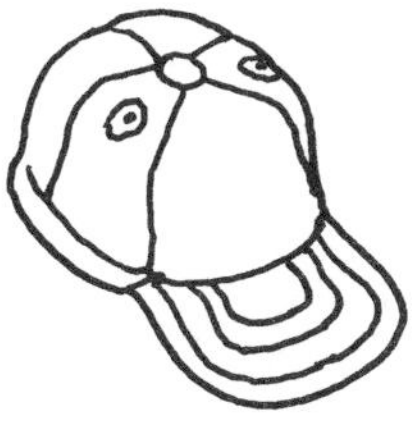 hat	 pan	 glad
2.  bat	 man	 sad	 cat
3.  sad	 mad	 rat	 fan
4.  can	 sack	 van	 backpack

Circle things in the picture that rhyme with **den**

hat

cat

ten

pail

dog

hen

pen

men

Help Ted find his way down the hill without hitting the shed. Follow the pictures that rhyme with **shed** .

red

bed

hen

bell

nest

pen

sled

shell

well

Finish

Say the names of the pictures. Color the pictures that rhyme with **met** .

jet	pet	hen
sled	net	wet
bed	pen	vet

Scholastic

Color the pictures on the crown that rhyme with **king**.

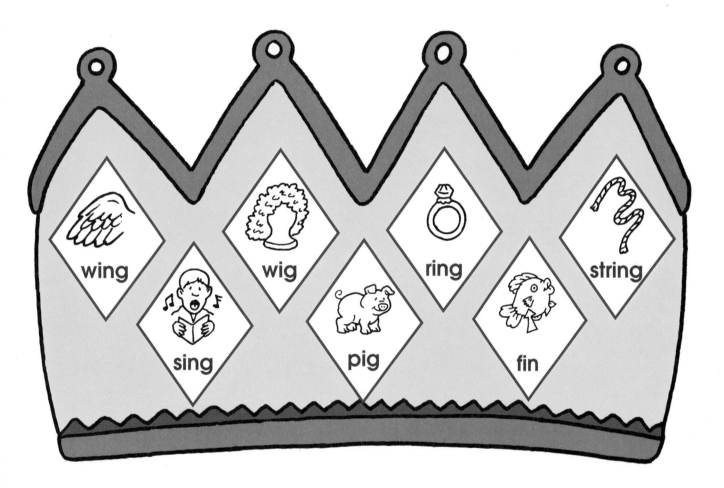

Read the story. Find and color the picture words in the story that rhyme with **big**.

pig   wig   twig   big

Once there was a  who wanted to go to the party. She put on her pretty pink . The

was way too . On the way to the party,

the got stuck on a . The lost

her .

Read the story. Find and color the picture words in the story that rhyme with **jog**.

   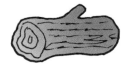      

frog   log   dog   hog

Freddy is a very large bull  . He is as big as

a . His best friends are a bull  and a

. Together they play leap  . See them

jump over the .

Say the names of the pictures in the balls.
Color the pictures that rhyme with **pop**   .

Scholastic

Read the story. Find and color the picture words in the story that rhyme with **dug**.

rug

bug

mug

hug

Once there was a lady . She liked to dance on

a . Her favorite dance was the jitter . She won a

first-place . Everyone gave her a  for being the

best dancing lady .

Randy hit a home run. Start at home plate and color the bases that rhyme with **fun** .

Scholastic

Look at the word on each basket. By changing the first letter, you can make new words. Use the letters on each snake to help you. Write the words on the blanks below each snake.

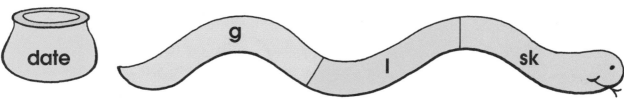

date   g   l   sk

1. _____ _____ _____

mail   f   p   t

2. _____ _____ _____

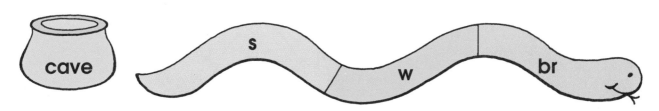

cave   s   w   br

3. _____ _____ _____

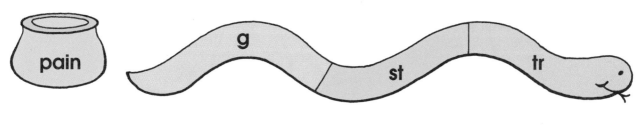

pain   g   st   tr

4. _____ _____ _____

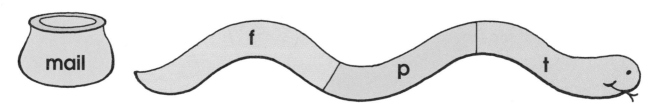

Long e *makes the sound you hear at the beginning of* **eagle**. *To help you remember the long-e sound, stretch out the beginning of the word like this:* e-e-e-eagle.

Help Ethan find the eagles that have pictures with the long-*e* sound. Color these eagles brown. If the picture on an eagle does not have a long-*e* sound, write *NO* on it.

 You have one of these on the end of your pencil. It is made of rubber. You need it when you make a mistake! It begins with the long-*e* sound. What is it? Write your name with a pencil. Now rub it off with the answer to the riddle.

Scholastic

Look at the word on each slide. By changing the first letter, you can make new words. Write the words on the slide.

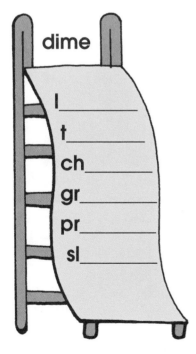
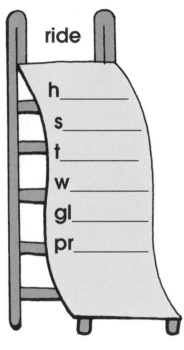
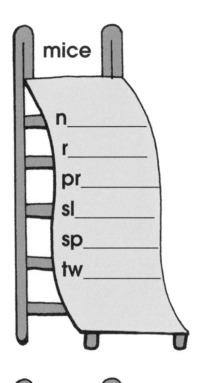
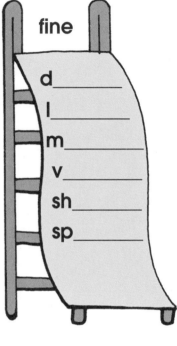
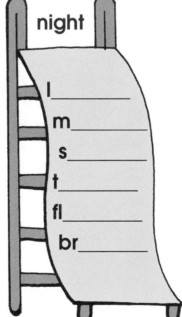

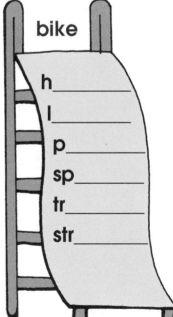

ride

h_____
s_____
t_____
w_____
gl_____
pr_____

mice

n_____
r_____
pr_____
sl_____
sp_____
tw_____

fine

d_____
l_____
m_____
v_____
sh_____
sp_____

dime

l_____
t_____
ch_____
gr_____
pr_____
sl_____

night

l_____
m_____
s_____
t_____
fl_____
br_____

bike

h_____
l_____
p_____
sp_____
tr_____
str_____

Scholastic

The **consonant-vowel-vowel-consonant rule:** *When two vowels come together, the first vowel is usually long and the second vowel is silent. You can say it this way, "When two vowels go walking, the first one does the talking!"*

Look at all the boats. Find the word that matches the picture and write it on the blank.

toast
road
soap
goat
toad
goal
foam
roast
coat

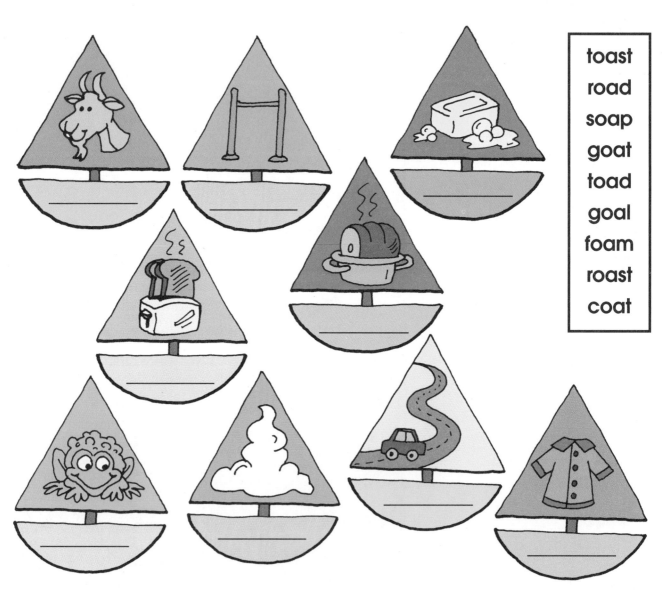

 The word *croak* has a long *o* and silent *a*. What is another word with a long *o* and silent *a* that names an animal that makes a croak sound?

Scholastic

Look at the word on each piece of fruit. Change the first letter to make a rhyming word. Write the word on the blank. Read your words to a friend.

1.

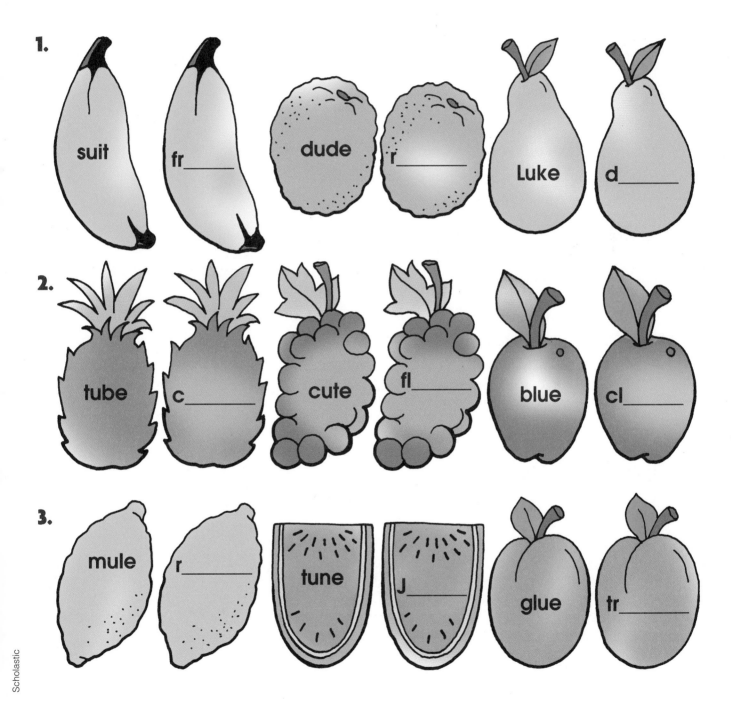

suit   fr_____   dude   r_____   Luke   d_____

2.

tube   c_____   cute   fl_____   blue   cl_____

3.

mule   r_____   tune   J_____   glue   tr_____

💡 **This is the color of the sky and the sea. It has a long-*u* sound. What is it?**

There are 26 letters in the alphabet. The vowels are **A**, **E**, **I**, **O**, and **U**. All the rest are consonants. Color each consonant yellow.

A B C D E F G H I

J K L M N O P Q

R S T U V W X Y Z

 A **consonant blend** is when two consonants are side by side in a word, and you hear both sounds blended together. For example, you hear both the **t** and the **r**, blended together, in the word **tree**.

Draw a red circle around the two consonants that are side by side.

tree

snow

fly

drum

Scholastic

Bl *makes the sound you hear at the beginning of the words* **Blake** *and* **bluebird**.

Draw a line from each **bl** word to its matching picture. Then draw a blue circle around the letters **bl** in each word.

black

blanket

blimp

blindfold

blocks

blizzard

blouse

 You have this inside you. It is red. Your heart pumps it through your body. It begins with *bl*. What is it?

Scholastic

Br *makes the sound you hear at the beginning of the words* **Brady** *and* **brontosaurus.**

Brady the brontosaurus has made a puzzle for you. Use the picture clues and the Word Box to help you. Write the answers in the puzzle next to the correct number.

Word Box

| brain | bride | broom | bridge |
| bread | brush | bricks | bracelet |

Across

2.

4.

6.

8.

Down

1.

3.

5.

7.

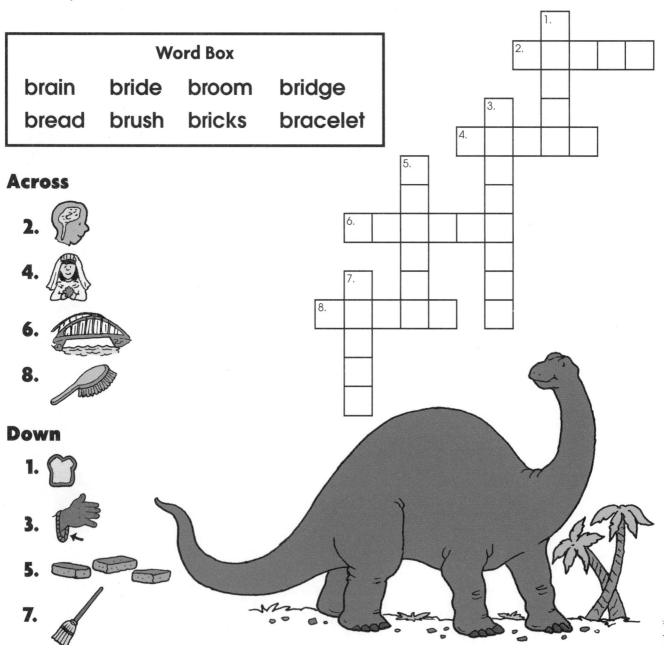

 This makes a blue or purple spot on your skin when you get hurt. It is sore when you push on it. It begins with *br*. **What is it?**

Scholastic

Cl *makes the sound you hear at the beginning of the words* **Clara** *and* **clown**.

See Clara juggle the balls. Color the balls orange that have pictures beginning with *cl*. Color all the other balls blue.

Now write "Clara" on her costume.

This is part of your room. You keep your clothes and shoes in it. It begins with *cl*.
What is it?

Scholastic

Cr *makes the sound you hear at the beginning of the words* **crazy** *and* **Crystal**.

Find out about the crazy things Crystal does in the sentences below. Fill in the blanks with **cr** to complete the words. Then write the number of the sentence in the box by the picture that matches it.

1. ___ystal wears a ___ash helmet to bed.

2. She makes ___ ispy, ___unchy ice ___eam.

3. She buys ___owns with her ___edit card.

4. She keeps her pet ___ab in a ___ib.

5. She feeds ___ackers to ___ocodiles.

6. Her glasses are ___ooked.

Dr *makes the sound you hear at the beginning of the words* **dragon** *and* **dream**.

This drowsy dragon wants to dream only about things that begin with **dr**. Color the pictures that it should dream about. If the picture does not begin with **dr**, mark an **X** on it.

Scholastic

Sn *makes the sound you hear at the beginning of the words* **Sniffles** *and* **snake***.*

Why is Sniffles the snake crying? He is lost! Help him find his way back to his mother. First, color only the pictures that begin with **sn**. Then use those clues to draw the path to Sniffles' mother.

Sp *makes the sound you hear at the beginning of the words* **Spike** *and* **spider**.

Spike the spider wants to catch **sp** words in his web. Color each picture that begins with **sp**. There are eight of them. Draw an **X** on the pictures that do not begin with **sp**.

 This begins with *sp*. **It is a green vegetable. It is good for you. Popeye eats it to make him strong. What is it?**

Phonics Practice Test

Read the questions. Color the bubble next to the correct answer.

Example

Which picture begins with **b**?

○ A

● B

○ C

○ D

1. Which of the letters is a **consonant**?

   ○ e

   ○ u

   ○ c

   ○ o

2. Which of the following is a **vowel**?

   ○ a

   ○ b

   ○ c

   ○ d

Scholastic

Phonics Practice Test

Read the questions. Color the bubble next to the correct answer.

3. Which picture begins with **d**?

○ A

○ B

○ C

○ D

4. Which picture ends with the **m sound**?

○ F

○ G

○ H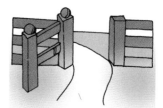

○ J

Scholastic

Phonics Practice Test

Read the questions. Color the bubble next to the correct answer.

5. Which picture has the **short-e sound**?

○ A

○ B

○ C

○ D

6. Which picture rhymes with **hop**?

○ F

○ G

○ H

○ J

Scholastic

Phonics Practice Test

Read the questions. Color the bubble next to the correct answer.

7. Which picture begins with the *br* **consonant blend**?

○ A

○ B

○ C

○ D

8. Which picture begins with the *dr* **consonant blend**?

○ F

○ G

○ H

○ J

Following Directions

"Pick up your clothes from the floor and put them in the hamper." "Clean Tucker's bowl and fill it with cat food." Directions are something all children are familiar with. In this section, your child will practice following directions. This is an essential skill that will prepare your child for test taking.

What to Do

Read the directions on each page with your child. Then have him or her complete the activity. Check to see how well your child did. Praise him or her for having done a good job. Point out how important following directions is in everyday life. For example: for building things, for making a cake, for finding places, etc.

Keep On Going!

Give your child directions for making sandwiches for the two of you. Then enjoy a lovely lunch together!

Can you help Sally finish her snow friend?

1 **Trace** the circles.

2 **Draw** a carrot nose.

3 **Add** three more details to the picture.

4 **Write** what details you added: _____

_____

_____

Scholastic

Make this rainbow colorful.

(**1**) **Look** at the chart below.

(**2**) **Color** each part of the rainbow using the chart.

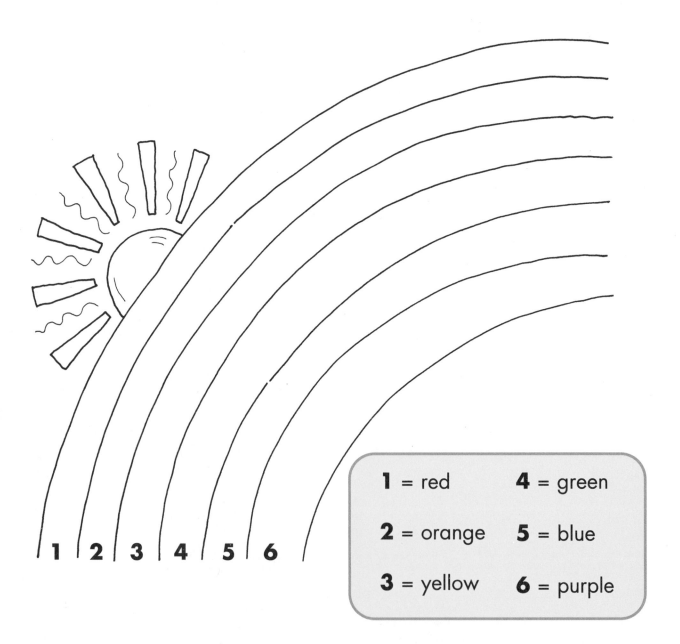

1 2 3 4 5 6

1 = red	**4** = green
2 = orange	**5** = blue
3 = yellow	**6** = purple

Scholastic

On Flag Day, many people in this country fly the American flag.

(**1**) **Read** the color words on the flag.

(**2**) **Color** each part of the flag.

(**3**) **Count** the stripes. **Write** the number here:_____

(**4**) **Write** two places where you have seen the flag.

_____

_____

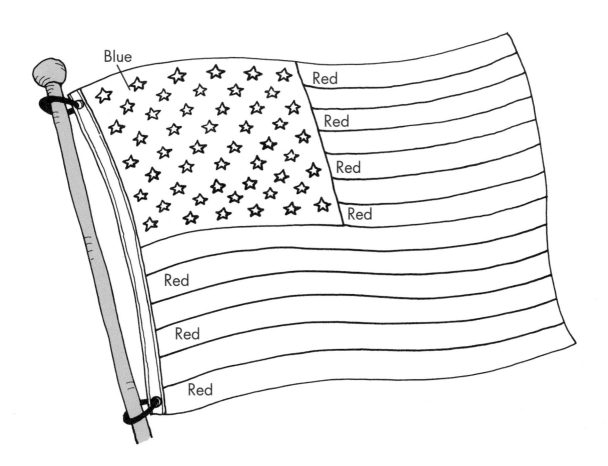

Scholastic

The kinara is a symbol of Kwanzaa.

(1) **Color** candles 1, 2, and 3 red.

(2) **Color** candle 4 black.

(3) **Color** candles 5, 6, and 7 green.

(4) **Color** the flames yellow.

(5) **Color** the rest of the kinara brown.

Scholastic

Imagine that tomorrow is your birthday.

1 **Color** the cake with your favorite colors.

2 **Cut** out the candles.

3 How old will you be on your next birthday?

Write that number here:_____

4 **Glue** that number of candles on the cake.

Scholastic

People in cities sometimes travel in taxicabs.

(1) Cut out the taxicabs.

(2) Glue a taxicab in front of the market.

(3) Glue a taxicab under the bridge.

(4) Glue a taxicab in front of the ice cream shop.

Scholastic

Following Directions Practice Test

Color the bubble next to the correct answer.

1. What insect is in the picture?

○ **A** ladybug

○ **B** bee

○ **C** ant

○ **D** butterfly

2. What insect is in the picture?

○ **F** ladybug

○ **G** bee

○ **H** cricket

○ **J** ant

Following Directions Practice Test

Color the bubble next to the correct answer.

3. Which object or creature might you see at the beach?

○ A

○ B

○ C

○ D

4. Which object or creature would **not** be at the beach?

○ F

○ G

○ H

○ J

Scholastic

Word Building

Your child is introduced to a variety of words in this section. Many of the words may already be familiar, and some may be new. These words will help your child to begin building vocabulary skills. Building a strong vocabulary is an important step in becoming a strong reader.

You will find many words from this section on the flash cards on pages 275–284.

What to Do

Have your child complete the activities on each page. On many of the pages there are pictures of the words. Point them out to your child. Review his or her work. Let your child know that he or she is doing a good job!

Keep On Going!

• Encourage your child to use the new words he or she is learning. Ask your child to help you write grocery lists, thank-you notes, and to-do lists.

• Make a list of high-frequency words—such as *the, to, and, was, said,* and so on. Pick a word of the day and have your child point out that word every time he or she sees it that day.

Trace and say the words.

b o o k

b o o k

t e a c h e r

t e a c h e r

b u s

b u s

f r i e n d s

f r i e n d s

Scholastic

Trace and say the words.

s	c	h	o	o	l
s	c	h	o	o	l

l	e	a	v	e	s
l	e	a	v	e	s

a	p	p	l	e	s
a	p	p	l	e	s

Scholastic

Reading & Math · Kindergarten (135)

Trace and say the words.

s	e	e
s	e	e

t	o	u	c	h
t	o	u	c	h

s	m	e	l	l
s	m	e	l	l

h	e	a	r
h	e	a	r

t	a	s	t	e
t	a	s	t	e

Scholastic

Trace and say the words.

c	c
a	a
r	r

t	t
r	r
u	u
c	c
k	k

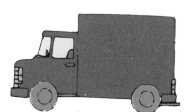

a	a
i	i
r	r
p	p
l	l
a	a
n	n
e	e

v	v
a	a
n	n

Scholastic

Trace and say the words.

r	r
a	a
i	i
n	n

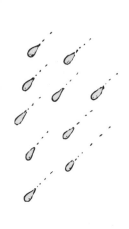

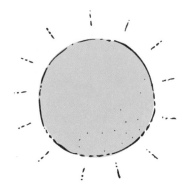

s	s
u	u
n	n

c	c
l	l
o	o
u	u
d	d
s	s

s	s
n	n
o	o
w	w

Scholastic

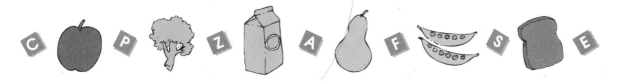

Trace and say the words.

b	b
r	r
e	e
a	a
d	d

m	m
i	i
l	l
k	k

f	f
r	r
u	u
i	i
t	t

v	e	g	e	t	a	b	l	e	s
v	e	g	e	t	a	b	l	e	s

Scholastic

Reading & Math · Kindergarten

Trace and say the words.

d	o	g
d	o	g

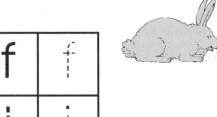

c	a	t
c	a	t

g	g
e	e
r	r
b	b
i	i
l	l

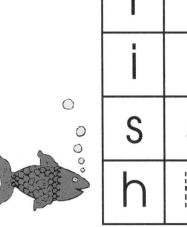

f	f
i	i
s	s
h	h

r	r
a	a
b	b
b	b
i	i
t	t

Scholastic

Trace the word and say it aloud.

and   and   and

cookies **and** milk

Write the word.

Cut out the letters at the bottom of the page and mix them up. Then paste them in the right squares to finish the sentence.

I like cookies ☐☐☐ milk.

Write the word to finish the sentence.

I like cookies _____ milk.

Write your own sentence using the word.

a n d

141

Trace the word and say it aloud.

big big big big

An elephant is **big**.

Write the word.

Cut out the letters at the bottom of the page and mix them up. Then paste them in the right squares to finish the sentence.

An elephant is ⬚⬚⬚.

Write the word to finish the sentence.

An elephant is ____.

Write your own sentence using the word.

Scholastic

b i g

I **can** ride a bike!

Trace the word and say it aloud.

can can can

Write the word.

Cut out the letters at the bottom of the page and mix them up. Then paste them in the right squares to finish the sentence.

I ☐☐☐ ride a bike!

Write the word to finish the sentence.

I _____ ride a bike!

Write your own sentence using the word.

Scholastic

c a n

143

Trace the word and say it aloud.

come come

Come here!

Write the word.

Cut out the letters at the bottom of the page and mix them up. Then paste them in the right squares to finish the sentence.

here!

Write the word to finish the sentence.

here!

Write your own sentence using the word.

Scholastic

Come

Trace the word and say it aloud.

down down

I'm going
down the stairs.

Write the word.

Cut out the letters at the bottom of the page and mix them up. Then paste them in the right squares to finish the sentence.

I'm going ⬚⬚⬚⬚ the stairs.

Write the word to finish the sentence.

I'm going _____ the stairs.

Write your own sentence using the word.

 d o w n

Trace the word and say it aloud.

for for for

*It's **for** you!*

Write the word.

Cut out the letters at the bottom of the page and mix them up. Then paste them in the right squares to finish the sentence.

It's ☐☐☐ you!

Write the word to finish the sentence.

It's ___ ___ ___ you!

Write your own sentence using the word.

Scholastic

f o r

Come **here**!

Trace the word and say it aloud.

here   here

Write the word.

Cut out the letters at the bottom of the page and mix them up. Then paste them in the right squares to finish the sentence.

Come [ ][ ][ ][ ] !

Write the word to finish the sentence.

Come ___ ___ ___ ___ !

Write your own sentence using the word.

Scholastic

h e r e

Trace the word and say it aloud.

I   I   I   I   I   I

I am six years old.

Write the word.

Cut out the letter at the bottom of the page. Then paste it in the square to finish the sentence.

☐ am six years old.

Write the word to finish the sentence.

___ am six years old.

Write your own sentence using the word.

I

Scholastic

Trace the word and say it aloud.

in in in in in in in

*The fox is **in** the box.*

Write the word.

Cut out the letters at the bottom of the page and mix them up. Then paste them in the right squares to finish the sentence.

The fox is ☐☐ the box.

Write the word to finish the sentence.

The fox is ___ the box.

Write your own sentence using the word.

i n

Trace the word and say it aloud.

is   is   is   is   is   is

The dog **is** happy.

Write the word.

Cut out the letters at the bottom of the page and mix them up. Then paste them in the right squares to finish the sentence.

The dog ☐☐ happy.

Write the word to finish the sentence.

The dog ___ happy.

Write your own sentence using the word.

Scholastic

i   s

Trace the word and say it aloud.

it it it it it it it

I made **it** myself.

Write the word.

Cut out the letters at the bottom of the page and mix them up. Then paste them in the right squares to finish the sentence.

I made ☐☐ myself.

Write the word to finish the sentence.

I made ___ ___ myself.

Write your own sentence using the word.

i t

Trace the word and say it aloud.

my my my

This is **my** cat.

Write the word.

Cut out the letters at the bottom of the page and mix them up. Then paste them in the right squares to finish the sentence.

This is ☐☐ cat.

Write the word to finish the sentence.

This is ___ cat.

Write your own sentence using the word.

m y

We **play** soccer.

Trace the word and say it aloud.

play play play

Write the word.

Cut out the letters at the bottom of the page and mix them up. Then paste them in the right squares to finish the sentence.

We ☐☐☐☐ soccer.

Write the word to finish the sentence.

We ___ ___ ___ ___ soccer.

Write your own sentence using the word.

p l a y

 153

Trace the word and say it aloud.

run   run   run

I can **run** *fast!*

Write the word.

Cut out the letters at the bottom of the page and mix them up. Then paste them in the right squares to finish the sentence.

I can ☐☐☐ fast!

Write the word to finish the sentence.

I can ___ ___ ___ fast!

Write your own sentence using the word.

Scholastic

r u n

Trace the word and say it aloud.

see see see

My glasses
help me **see**.

Write the word.

Cut out the letters at the bottom of the page and mix them up. Then paste them in the right squares to finish the sentence.

My glasses help me ☐☐☐.

Write the word to finish the sentence.

My glasses help me ___ ___ ___.

Write your own sentence using the word.

s e e

155

Trace the word and say it aloud.

the   the   the

The sun is in the sky.

Write the word.

Cut out the letters at the bottom of the page and mix them up. Then paste them in the right squares to finish the sentence.

sun is in the sky.

Write the word to finish the sentence.

____ ____ ____ sun is in the sky.

Write your own sentence using the word.

Scholastic

The

Trace the word and say it aloud.

we we we we

We are on the same team.

Write the word.

Cut out the letters at the bottom of the page and mix them up. Then paste them in the right squares to finish the sentence.

☐☐ are on the same team.

Write the word to finish the sentence.

_____ are on the same team.

Write your own sentence using the word.

We

Trace the word and say it aloud.

you you you

Hello, how are **you**?

Write the word.

Cut out the letters at the bottom of the page and mix them up. Then paste them in the right squares to finish the sentence.

Hello, how are ☐☐?

Write the word to finish the sentence.

Hello, how are _____?

Write your own sentence using the word.

Scholastic

y o u

Trace the word and say it aloud.

am am am am

I **am** very tall.

Write the word.

Cut out the letters at the bottom of the page and mix them up. Then paste them in the right squares to finish the sentence.

I ☐☐ very tall.

Write the word to finish the sentence.

I ___ very tall.

Write your own sentence using the word.

a m

159

Trace the word and say it aloud.

are are are

Hello, how **are** you?

Write the word.

Cut out the letters at the bottom of the page and mix them up. Then paste them in the right squares to finish the sentence.

Hello, how ☐☐☐ you?

Write the word to finish the sentence.

Hello, how _____ you?

Write your own sentence using the word.

Scholastic

a r e

Trace the word and say it aloud.

came came

The bear
came out.

Write the word.

Cut out the letters at the bottom of the page and mix them up. Then paste them in the right squares to finish the sentence.

The bear ☐☐☐☐ out.

Write the word to finish the sentence.

The bear ___ ___ ___ out.

Write your own sentence using the word.

c a m e

Trace the word and say it aloud.

have have

I **have** a new pet.

Write the word.

Cut out the letters at the bottom of the page and mix them up. Then paste them in the right squares to finish the sentence.

I ☐☐☐☐ a new pet.

Write the word to finish the sentence.

I _____ a new pet.

Write your own sentence using the word.

Scholastic

h a v e

Trace the word and say it aloud.

I **like** to swim.

like   like   like

Write the word.

Cut out the letters at the bottom of the page and mix them up. Then paste them in the right squares to finish the sentence.

I ⬚⬚⬚⬚ to swim.

Write the word to finish the sentence.

I _____ to swim.

Write your own sentence using the word.

like

Trace the word and say it aloud.

ran ran ran

*I just **ran** in a race.*

Write the word.

Cut out the letters at the bottom of the page and mix them up. Then paste them in the right squares to finish the sentence.

I just ☐☐☐ in a race.

Write the word to finish the sentence.

I just _____ in a race.

Write your own sentence using the word.

Scholastic

r a n

Trace the word and say it aloud.

she she she

She is my best friend.

Write the word.

Cut out the letters at the bottom of the page and mix them up. Then paste them in the right squares to finish the sentence.

is my best friend.

Write the word to finish the sentence.

_____ is my best friend.

Write your own sentence using the word.

S h e

(165)

Scholastic

Trace the word and say it aloud.

want   want

Do you **want**
some more?

Write the word.

Cut out the letters at the bottom of the page and mix them up. Then paste them in the right squares to finish the sentence.

Do you ⬚⬚⬚⬚ some more?

Write the word to finish the sentence.

Do you ___ ___ ___ ___ some more?

Write your own sentence using the word.

w a n t

Scholastic

What time is it?

Trace the word and say it aloud.

what   what

Write the word.

Cut out the letters at the bottom of the page and mix them up. Then paste them in the right squares to finish the sentence.

time is it?

Write the word to finish the sentence.

_____ _____ _____ _____ time is it?

Write your own sentence using the word.

W h a t

Who wants to *play?*

Trace the word and say it aloud.

who who who

Write the word.

Cut out the letters at the bottom of the page and mix them up. Then paste them in the right squares to finish the sentence.

[ ][ ][ ] wants to play?

Write the word to finish the sentence.

_____ wants to play?

Write your own sentence using the word.

Scholastic

W h o

Choose words from the Word Box to complete the crossword puzzle.

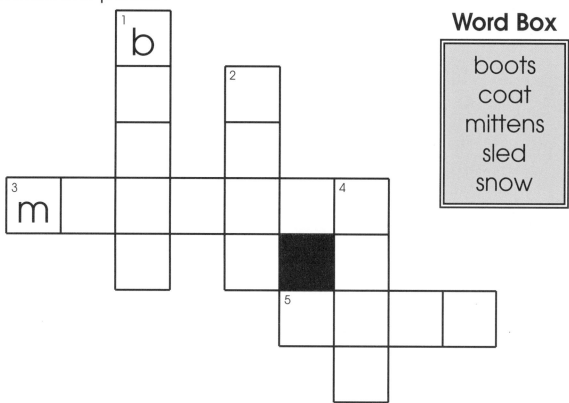

Word Box

boots
coat
mittens
sled
snow

Across

3.

5.

Down

1.

2.

4.

Scholastic

Choose words from the Word Box to complete the crossword puzzle.

Word Box

ball
blocks
doll
puzzle
truck
bat

Across

3.

5.

Down

1.

2. (ball image)

4. (doll image)

5.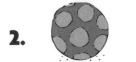

Scholastic

Choose words from the Word Box to complete the crossword puzzle.

Word Box

coat
pants
shirt
socks
sweater

¹S		²C		

³					

⁴P

Across

1.

3.

4.

Down

2.

3.

Scholastic

Choose words from the Word Box to complete the crossword puzzle.

Word Box

balloons
cake
candles
gifts
hats

Across

3.

5.

Down

1.

2.

4.

Scholastic

Choose words from the Word Box to complete the crossword puzzle.

Word Box

basket
bee
birds
egg
flower

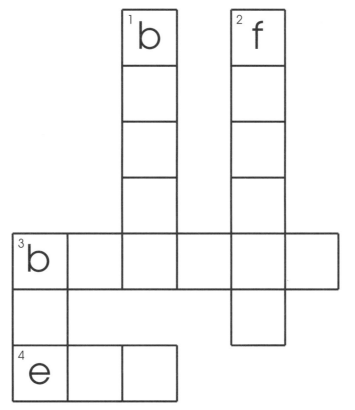

Scholastic

Choose words from the Word Box to complete the crossword puzzle.

Word Box

ant
bee
butterfly
ladybug
slug

Choose words from the Word Box to complete the crossword puzzle.

¹ f ² l [ ] [ ] [ ] ³ r

⁴ p [ ] [ ]

⁵ s [ ] [ ] [ ]

Word Box

flower
leaves
pots
roots
seeds

Scholastic

Find the hidden word that matches the picture.
Circle it. Then write it on the blank.

1.  **playballink**

_____

2.  **totigered**

_____

3.  **sunopenlip**

_____

4.  **winnetnest**

_____

5.  **kidqueenby**

_____

6.  **girlduckis**

_____

Read each direction. Write the word
on the line.

1. Write a word that starts with **p.** _____

2. Write a word that starts with **m.** _____

3. Write a word that starts with **b.** _____

4. Write a word that starts with **s.** _____

5. Write a word that starts with **g.** _____

6. Write a word that starts with **t.** _____

7. Write a word that starts with **w.** _____

8. Write a word that starts with **a.** _____

Scholastic

Read each direction. Write the word on the line.

1. Write a word that ends with **t.** _____

2. Write a word that ends with **n.** _____

3. Write a word that ends with **k.** _____

4. Write a word that ends with **s.** _____

5. Write a word that ends with **g.** _____

6. Write a word that ends with **r.** _____

7. Write a word that ends with **w.** _____

8. Write a word that ends with **e.** _____

Think and draw.

1. Draw a △ **ABOVE** the car.

4. Draw a △ **ON** the dinosaur.

2. Draw a △ **BELOW** the bat.

5. Draw a △ **BEHIND** the class.

3. Draw a △ **UNDER** the snail.

6. Draw a △ **AHEAD** of the cowboy.

Scholastic

Word Building Practice Test

Color the bubble next to the correct answer.

Example

The word **cloud** matches which picture?

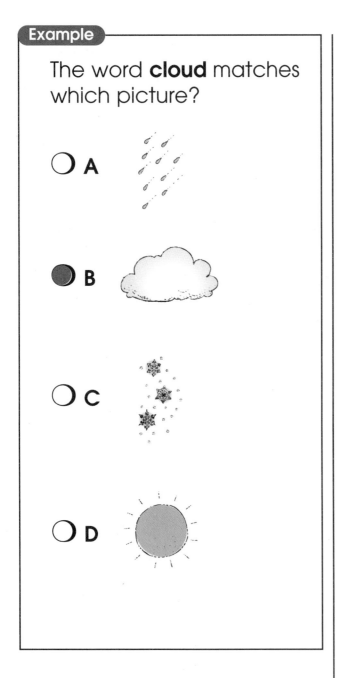

○ A

● B

○ C

○ D

1. Which picture shows something you eat?

○ A

○ B

○ C

○ D

2. Which picture shows something you might play with?

○ F

○ G

○ H

○ J

Word Building Practice Test

Color the bubble next to the correct answer.

3. Which word completes the following sentence?

I like cookies _____ milk.

○ **A** at

○ **B** and

○ **C** but

○ **D** big

4. Which word completes the following sentence?

The cat is _____ the house.

○ **F** in

○ **G** over

○ **H** my

○ **J** have

Scholastic

Word Building Practice Test

Color the bubble next to the correct answer.

				k	s

				o	o	

5. Which word fits in the boxes above?

○ A

○ B

○ C

○ D

6. Which word fits in the boxes above?

○ F

○ G

○ H

○ J

Scholastic

Word Building Practice Test

Color the bubble next to the correct answer.

7. Which word find has the word that matches the picture?

○ **A**   kidgirlbee

○ **B**   toballby

○ **C**   playeggink

○ **D**   flowerduckis

8. Which word find has the word that matches the picture?

○ **F**   totigered

○ **G**   opensunlip

○ **H**   eggqueenest

○ **J**   playgirlip

Scholastic

Reading Readiness

In this section, your child is introduced to important reading skills. These skills will show your child how to make meaning out of what he or she reads.

What to Do

Have your child complete the activities on each page. Review his or her answers. Let your child know that he or she is doing an excellent job.

Keep On Going!

Ask your child questions about his or her day at school. *What did you do first? Next? Last? How did you make that art project?* Have your child look at objects and tell how they are alike and different. Or read a book with your child. Have your child look at the cover of the book and predict what the story will be about. Have your child identify where the story takes place. Have him or her describe the characters in the story. When you have finished reading, ask your child to retell the story in his or her own words.

Think and draw.

1. Draw a ✳ to the **LEFT** of the tree.

2. Draw a ✳ to the **RIGHT** of the apple.

3. Draw a ✳ to the **RIGHT** of the pencil.

4. Draw a ✳ to the **LEFT** of the box.

5. Draw a ✳ to the **LEFT** of the circle.

6. Draw a ✳ to the **RIGHT** of the ladder.

Scholastic

Look at the pictures.
Which comes first? Write **1**.
Which comes next? Write **2**.
Which comes last? Write **3**.
Then write the story the pictures show.

_____

- -

_____

- -

_____

- -

_____

- -

_____

Look at the pictures.
Which comes first? Write **1**.
Which comes next? Write **2**.
Which comes last? Write **3**.
Then write the story the pictures show.

_____

- -

_____

- -

_____

- -

_____

- -

_____

Scholastic

Look at the pictures.

Which comes first? Write **1**.

Which comes next? Write **2**.

Which comes after that? Write **3**.

Which comes last? Write **4**.

Then write the story the pictures show.

Scholastic

Look at the big picture.
Which small picture comes *next*?
Check ✔ that picture. Tell how you know.

_____

_____

_____

_____

_____

_____

Scholastic

Look at the big picture.
Which small picture comes *next*?
Check ✔ that picture. Tell how you know.

_____

- -

_____

- -

_____

- -

_____

- -

_____

Scholastic

Devin made a Valentine's Day card for his grandmother.

(1) **Look** at the pictures below.

(2) What happened first? **Write** a 1 under that picture.

(3) What happened next? **Write** a 2 under that picture.

(4) What happened last? **Write** a 3 under that picture.

_____   _____   _____

Scholastic

Construction workers build buildings.

(1) **Look** at the pictures below.

(2) What happened first? **Write** a 1 under that picture.

(3) What happened next? **Write** a 2 under that picture.

(4) What happened last? **Write** a 3 under that picture.

(5) **Color** the pictures any way you like.

_____   _____   _____

There are many kinds of cows.

(1) **Draw** a circle around the cow that does not match.

(2) **Draw** a triangle around the cow that does not match.

(3) **Draw** a square around the cow that does not match.

Scholastic

Find the things that do not match.

(**1**) **Look** at the pictures.

(**2**) **Circle** the picture in each row that does not match the others.

(**3**) **Color** all the starfish orange.

(**4**) **Color** all the pails blue.

(**5**) **Color** all the shovels red.

Scholastic

Look at the big picture.
Which small picture came *before*?
Check ✔ that picture. Tell how you know.

_____

_____

_____

_____

_____

_____

Scholastic

Look at the big picture.
Which small picture came *before*?
Check ✔ that picture. Tell how you know.

Scholastic

Look at the group.
Circle the word that names it. Then finish the sentence.

birds
fish
trees

1. This is a group of _____ .

books
jobs
trucks

2. This is a group of _____ .

clothes
animals
buildings

3. This is a group of _____ .

Scholastic

Look at the pictures.
Draw an **X** on the one that is NOT part of the group.
Then write the name of the group.

1. These are _____ .

2. These are _____ .

3. These are _____ .

4. These are _____ .

Have you ever looked up in the sky and seen a cloud that is shaped like an animal or a person? Big, white, puffy clouds float along like soft marshmallows. In cartoons, people can sit on clouds and bounce on them. But clouds are really just tiny drops of water floating in the air. You can understand what being in a cloud is like when it is foggy. Fog is a cloud on the ground!

Read each sentence below. If the sentence is true or could really happen, color the cloud blue. If the sentence is make-believe, color it orange.

1. Clouds float in the sky.

2. A dog sleeps on a cloud.

3. Clouds are made of tiny drops of water.

4. Animal shapes in clouds are made by the Cloud Fairy.

5. Clouds are big blobs of whipped cream.

6. Clouds are made of marshmallows.

7. Fog is a cloud on the ground.

8. Birds can hop around on clouds.

Scholastic

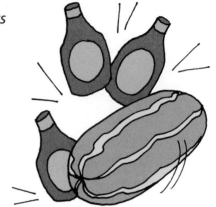

*Story events that can really happen are **real**. Story events that are make-believe are **fantasy**.*

At night, Mr. Lee locked the store and went home. That's when the fun began! The ketchup bottles stood in rows like bowling pins. Then the watermelon rolled down the aisle and knocked them down. The chicken wings flew around the room. Cans of soup stacked themselves higher and higher until they laughed so hard that they tumbled over. Carrots danced with bananas. Then it was morning. "Get back in your places!" called the milk jug. "Mr. Lee is coming!" Mr. Lee opened the door and went right to work.

Circle the cans that are make-believe.

1.  ketchup bottles and a watermelon bowling

2.  a talking milk jug

3.  dancing bananas

4.  chicken wings that can fly all by themselves

5. Mr. Lee went to work.

6.  laughing soup cans

7.  Mr. Lee went home at night.

8. dancing carrots

9.  a grocery store

Scholastic

Reading Readiness Practice Test

Color the bubble next to the correct answer.

1. Which picture shows an * on the **left** of the tree?

○ **A**

○ **B**

○ **C**

○ **D**

2. Which would you do **first** to make a cake?

○ **F**   add an egg to cake mix

○ **G**   put cake mix into a bowl

○ **H**   eat the cake

○ **J**   add milk to cake mix

Reading Readiness Practice Test

Color the bubble next to the correct answer.

3. Which comes **last** when you cook scrambled eggs?

    ◯ **A**   crack the eggs into a bowl

    ◯ **B**   scramble the eggs

    ◯ **C**   put eggs on plate and eat them

    ◯ **D**   turn on the stove

4. Which picture does **not** belong in the group?

    ◯ **F**

    ◯ **G**

    ◯ **H**

    ◯ **J**

Reading Readiness Practice Test

Color the bubble next to the correct answer.

5. Which picture does **not** belong in the group?

○ A

○ B

○ C

○ D

6. Which event caused a fire?

○ F   A candle fell onto a rug.

○ G   Water was thrown on the fire.

○ H   Firefighters arrived at the scene.

○ J   Smokey the bear ran away.

Reading Readiness Practice Test

Color the bubble next to the correct answer.

7. Which event could really happen?

     ○ **A**   Henry rides an alligator to school.

     ○ **B**   Henry drives a car to the moon.

     ○ **C**   Henry has dinner with a dinosaur.

     ○ **D**   Henry carries a flag in a parade.

8. Which event is make-believe?

     ○ **F**   clouds floating in the sky

     ○ **G**   a fish climbing a tree

     ○ **H**   flowers growing in the sun

     ○ **J**   whales playing in the ocean

Scholastic

Thinking Skills

"What's the problem?" "How can I solve it?" Throughout his or her life, your child will face those questions. Knowing how to think through a problem in order to solve it is an important life skill. The activities in this section will help your child develop important thinking strategies.

What to Do

Have your child complete the activities on each page. Ask how he or she decided on the answers. The explanations will help your child identify the problem-solving strategies he or she uses.

Keep On Going!

Play a "What Would You Do?" game with your child. Present your child with a problem and have him or her tell you how he or she would go about solving it. For example: Your dog comes into the house with muddy feet. Or, you want to go to the movies but you have already spent all of your allowance.

Put an **X** in the correct box.

1. Which belongs in a toy store?

2. Which belongs on a boat?

3. Which belongs in a zoo?

4. Which belongs on a desk?

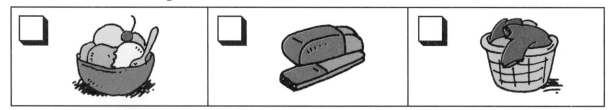

5. Which belongs in the refrigerator?

Scholastic

Put an **X** in the correct box.

1. Which belongs in a music store?

2. Which belongs in the art room?

3. Which belongs at the doctor's office?

4. Which belongs in a castle?

5. Which belongs at a circus?

Scholastic

Write the correct word on the blank.

1. Which does **NOT** belong?

| bulb  | saw  | hammer  |

The _____ does not belong.

2. Which does **NOT** belong?

| bananas  | potato | lemon |

The _____ does not belong.

3. Which does **NOT** belong?

| blanket  | pillow | rope  |

The _____ does not belong.

4. Which does **NOT** belong?

| dollar  | pig  | penny |

The _____ does not belong.

Scholastic

Find three things that are like each other.
Circle the three things. Write the three words below.

 fish	 cow	 globe	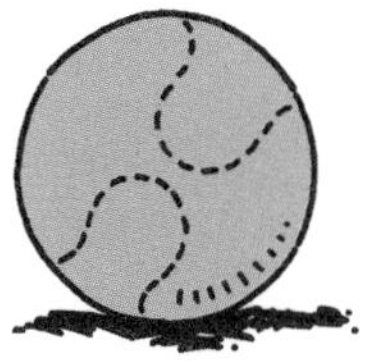 ball
 key	 milk	 sled	 marble

Thinking Skills Practice Test

Color the bubble next to the correct answer.

1. Which of the things shown could you eat?

○ A

○ B

○ C

○ D

2. Which of the things shown is something you could **not** eat.

○ F

○ G

○ H

○ J

Scholastic

Thinking Skills Practice Test

Color the bubble next to the correct answer.

3. Which of the things shown does **not** belong?

○ A

○ B

○ C

○ D

4. Which of the things shown can you wear?

○ F

○ G

○ H

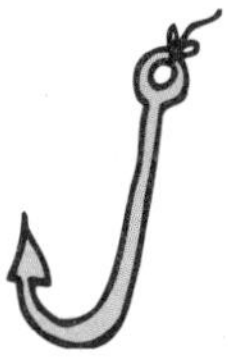

○ J

Numbers & Number Concepts

In this section, your child reviews numbers 1–10 and is introduced to numbers 11–20. The number concepts will get your child ready for addition and subtraction.

What to Do
Read the directions on each page with your child. Then have your child complete the activities. Review them together. Praise your child for a job well done!

Keep On Going!
Go on a nature walk with your child. Have him or her collect items such as rocks, leaves, flowers, shells, pine cones, or other objects you see along the way. When home, have your child group the same objects together and count them. Ask which group has the smallest number and which has the largest number.

Circle the correct number of objects.

Example		
1	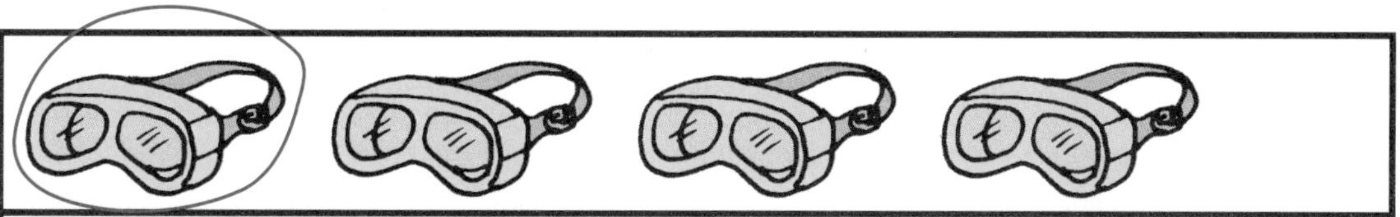
6	
4	
10	
5	
2	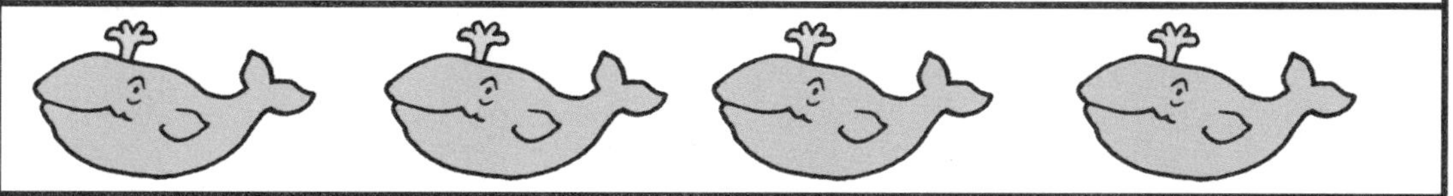
7	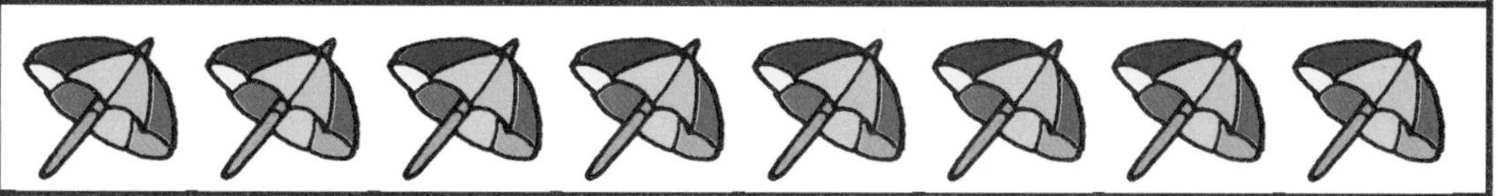
8	
3	
9	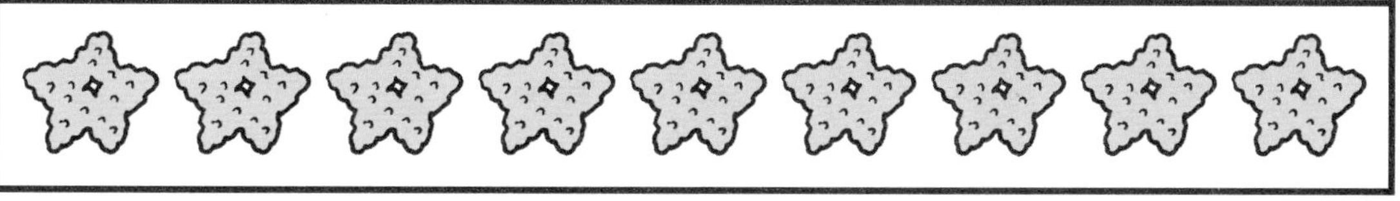

Connect the dots from **1** to **10**. Color the pictures.

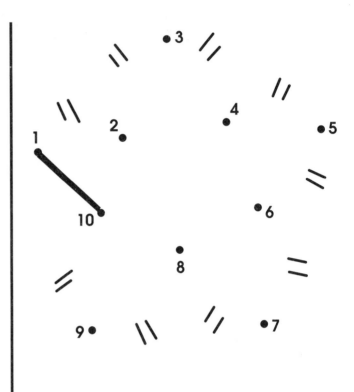
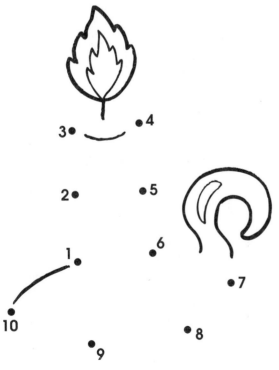
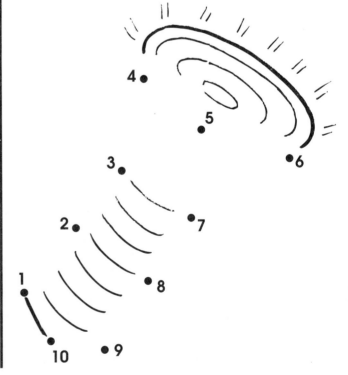

Scholastic

eleven

Number Practice

Trace the number.

Write the number.

Trace the word.

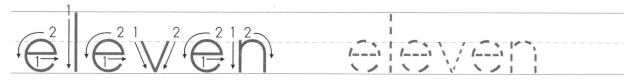

Write the word.

Number Hunt

Circle every number 11.

9	25	2	4	26	4	0	3	1	11
11	3	25	3	9	8	11	2	21	5
3	0	5	4	3	20	0	5	8	11
1	3	7	11	8	10	14	9	3	11

Scholastic

Cut out 11 pennies. Paste them in the piggybank.

Draw 11 windows on the building.

216

Number Practice

Trace the number.

Write the number.

Trace the word.

$\uparrow$twelve twelve

Write the word.

Number Hunt

Circle every number 12.

8	13	0	3	12	9	25	12	4	26
12	25	3	9	8	1	2	21	5	7
24	3	12	5	4	3	20	0	5	8
3	0	29	12	8	10	14	9	3	12

Scholastic

Cut out 12 apples. Paste them on the tree.

Draw 12 flowers.

Scholastic

Number Practice

Trace the number.

Write the number.

Trace the word.

Write the word.

Number Hunt

Circle every number 13.

9	25	2	13	26	4	0	13	1	8
21	5	7	3	9	8	1	2	12	3
16	13	20	13	5	24	3	0	5	4
13	19	8	10	14	9	0	29	9	13

Scholastic

Cut out 13 cupcakes. Paste them below.

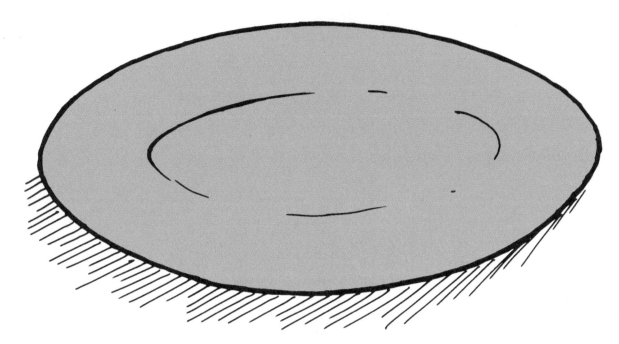

Draw 13 balloons for the party.

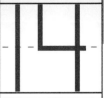

fourteen

Number Practice

Trace the number.

Write the number.

Trace the word.

Write the word.

Number Hunt

Circle every number 14.

0	14	1	8	13	9	25	2	4	26
21	5	7	14	3	25	3	9	8	14
8	14	24	3	0	5	14	3	20	0
3	0	29	14	3	7	14	8	10	14

Scholastic

Cut out 14 penguins. Paste them on the icebergs.

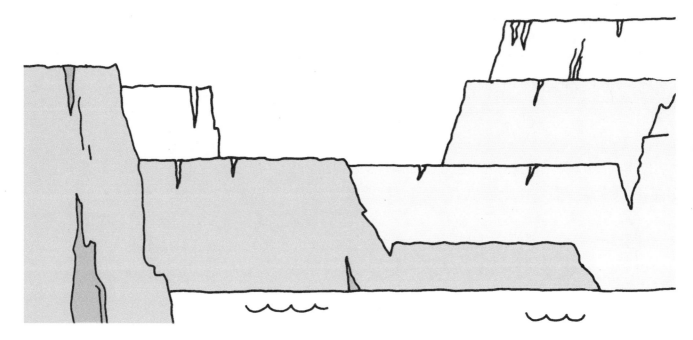

Draw 14 snowflakes in the sky.

fifteen

Number Practice

Trace the number.

Write the number.

Trace the word.

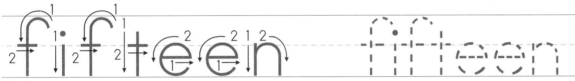

Write the word.

Number Hunt

Circle every number 15.

8	13	9	25	15	4	26	4	0	3
25	15	9	8	1	2	21	5	7	15
5	4	3	20	15	5	8	16	24	3
15	3	7	19	8	10	15	9	3	0

Cut out 15 chicks. Paste them in the barnyard.

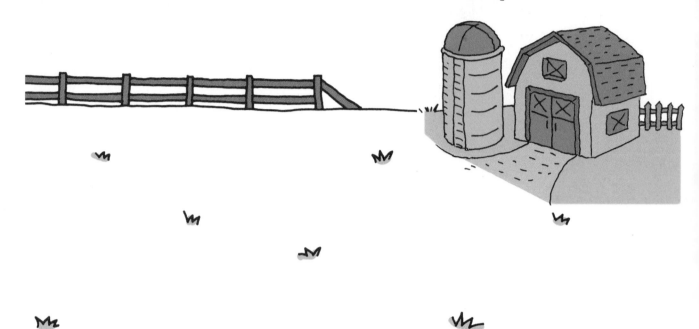

Draw 15 eggs.

Number Practice

Trace the number.

16 16 16 16 16 16

Write the number.

Trace the word.

 sixteen

Write the word.

Number Hunt

Circle every number 16.

10	16	9	8	13	9	25	2	16	26
21	5	16	12	3	25	3	9	5	16
16	0	5	8	16	24	3	0	16	1
3	0	29	16	3	7	19	8	0	3

Scholastic

Cut out 16 turtles. Paste them on the rocks.

Draw 16 squares on the turtle shell.

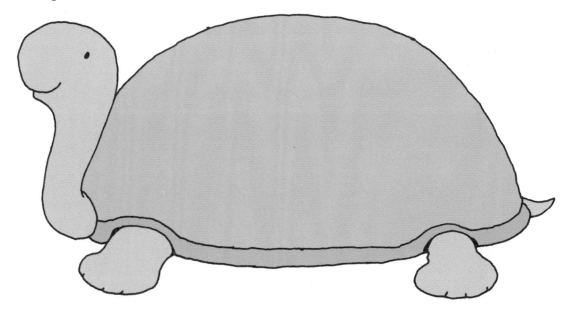

Scholastic

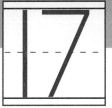
Number Practice

Trace the number.

Write the number.

Trace the word.

Write the word.

Number Hunt

Circle every number 17.

17	3	1	8	13	9	25	2	17	26
21	17	7	12	3	25	3	9	8	1
8	16	24	3	0	17	4	3	20	0
3	17	29	1	3	7	17	8	10	14

Scholastic

Cut out 17 seahorses. Paste them in the water.

Draw 17 clams on the beach.

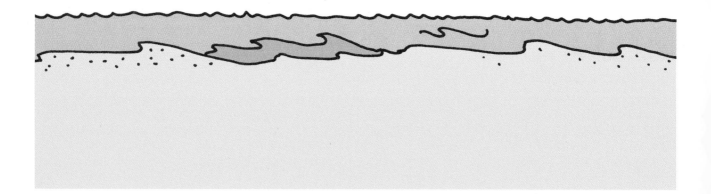

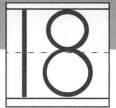
Number Practice

Trace the number.

Write the number.

Trace the word.

Write the word.

Number Hunt

Circle every number 18.

2	16	24	18	0	5	4	3	20	18
0	3	1	8	13	9	25	2	4	26
18	0	29	1	3	7	19	8	18	14
21	18	7	12	3	25	3	9	8	18

Scholastic

Cut out 18 pretzels. Paste them on the plate.

Draw 18 pieces of popcorn.

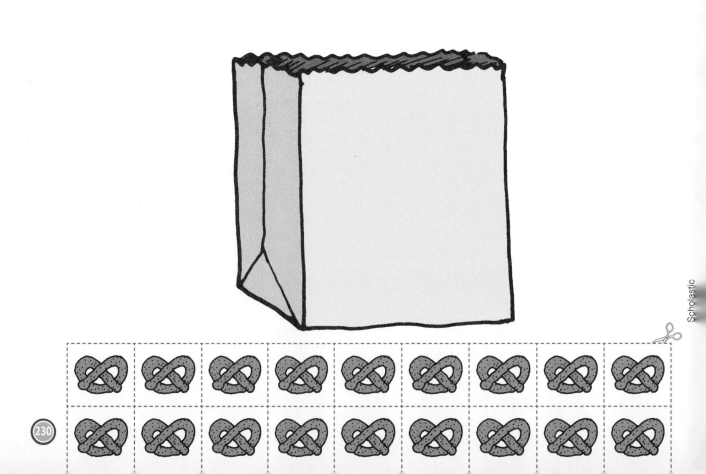

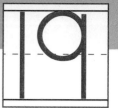
Number Practice

Trace the number.

Write the number.

Trace the word.

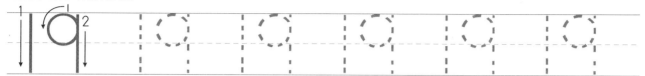

Write the word.

Number Hunt

Circle every number 19.

19	5	7	12	3	25	3	19	8	1
9	25	2	4	26	4	19	3	1	8
8	19	24	3	0	5	4	3	20	0
7	19	0	29	1	19	7	19	8	10

Scholastic

Cut out 19 strawberries. Paste them in the bowl.

Draw 19 ants in the grass.

Number Practice

Trace the number.

 20   20   20   20

Write the number.

Trace the word.

   twenty

Write the word.

Number Hunt

Circle every number 20.

20	0	29	1	3	7	19	20	10	14
21	5	7	12	20	25	3	9	8	1
8	20	24	3	0	5	4	20	20	0
0	3	1	20	13	9	25	2	4	26

Scholastic

Cut out 20 dragonflies. Paste them above the pond.

Draw 20 fish swimming.

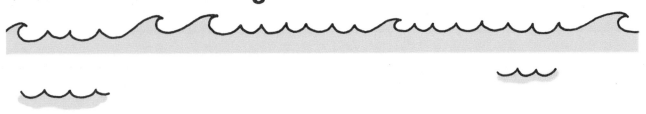

Count the spots on each ladybug.

Circle the correct number word.

	one five		two seven
	fourteen sixteen		nineteen fifteen
	ten eleven		twenty twelve
	eighteen thirteen		nine eight
	seven four		seven three

Scholastic

Draw a circle around each group of 11.

Draw a square around each group of 12.

Scholastic

Draw an oval around each group of 13.

Draw a rectangle around each group of 14.

Scholastic

Draw a circle around each group of 15.

Draw a rectangle around each group of 16.

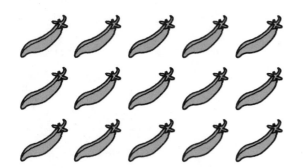

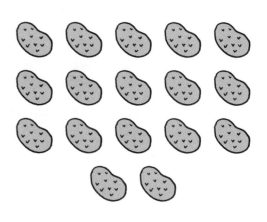

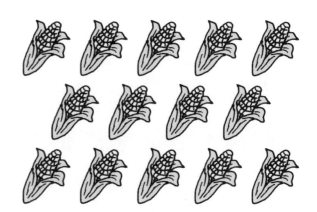

Draw a circle around each group of 17.

Draw a square around each group of 18.

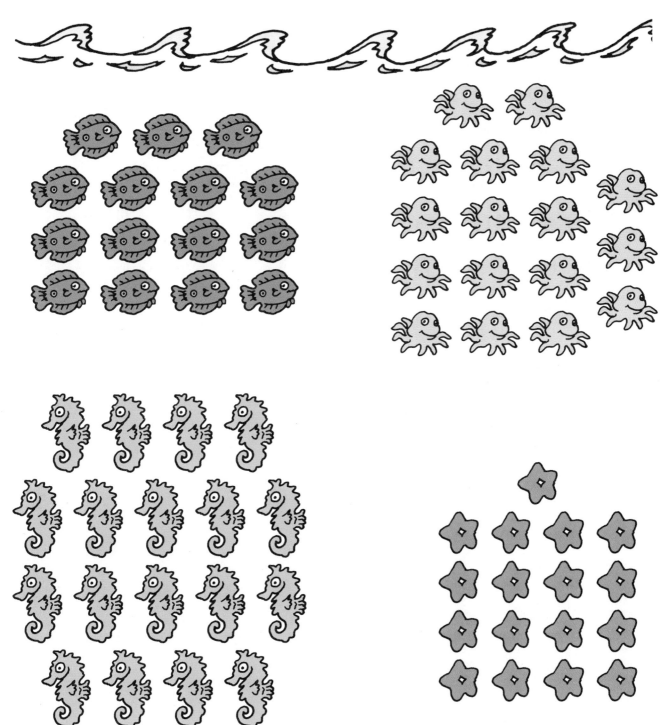

Draw a circle around each group of 19.

Draw a square around each group of 20.

Scholastic

Color. **11** = yellow **12** = black **13** = blue

14 = white **15** = orange **16** = green

17 = red **18** = purple **19** = brown

20 = pink

Connect the dots from 1 to 20.

Scholastic

Color the bows on the tails to match the number above each kite.

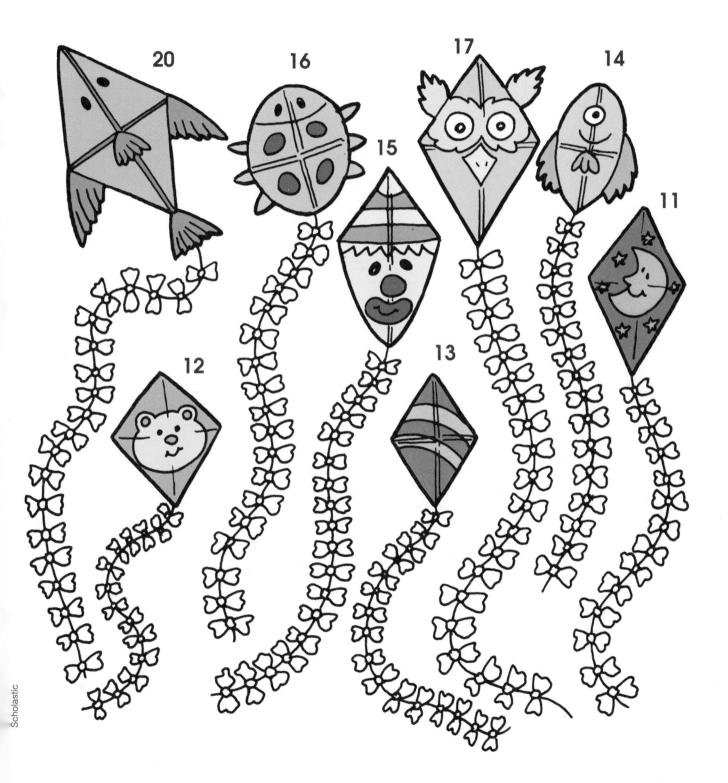

Circle the pictures with the same number as in the first picture.

Scholastic

Draw a line to match the groups with the same number.

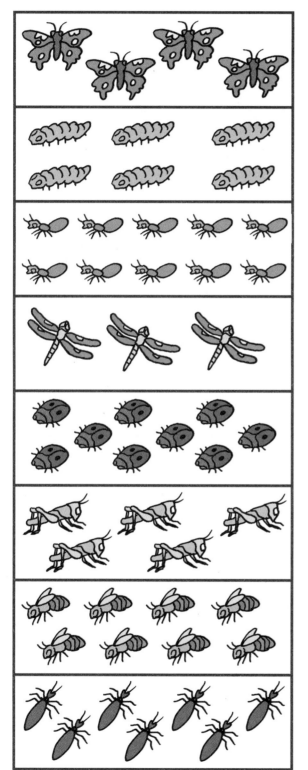
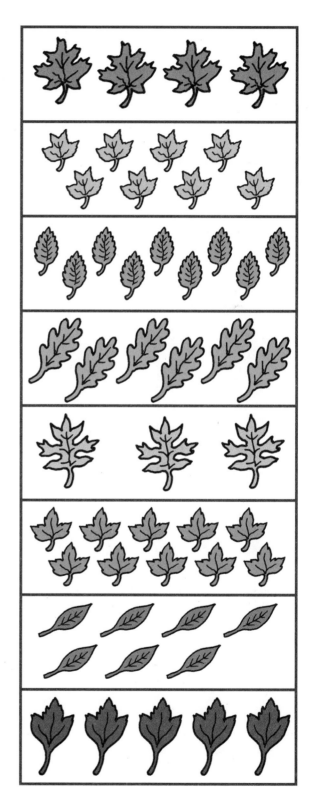

Scholastic

Numbers & Number Concepts Practice Test

Color the bubble next to the correct answer.

1. Which number word comes **after** twelve?

    ○ A   fifteen

    ○ B   twenty

    ○ C   thirteen

    ○ D   eleven

2. Which number word comes **before** fourteen.

    ○ F   nineteen

    ○ G   eleven

    ○ H   thirteen

    ○ J   sixteen

Scholastic

Numbers & Number Concepts Practice Test

Color the bubble next to the correct answer.

Example

How many pens are shown?

- ● **A** 10
- ○ **B** 14
- ○ **C** 12
- ○ **D** 11

---

3. How many backpacks are shown?

- ○ **A** 9
- ○ **B** 10
- ○ **C** 11
- ○ **D** 14

---

4. How many crayons are shown?

- ○ **F** 8
- ○ **G** 9
- ○ **H** 10
- ○ **J** 11

Numbers & Number Concepts Practice Test

Color the bubble next to the correct answer.

5. How many strawberries are shown?

   ○ **A**   17

   ○ **B**   18

   ○ **C**   19

   ○ **D**   20

6. How many pears are shown?

   ○ **F**   12

   ○ **G**   13

   ○ **H**   14

   ○ **J**   15

Scholastic

Numbers & Number Concepts Practice Test

Color the bubble next to the correct answer.

7. How many trumpets are shown?

○ **A** 13

○ **B** 12

○ **C** 11

○ **D** 10

8. How many violins are shown?

○ **F** 15

○ **G** 16

○ **H** 17

○ **J** 18

Shapes & Patterns

In this section, your child will identify a variety of shapes. Recognizing shapes helps children begin to develop geometry skills.

Your child will also learn to identify the sequence of objects in patterns and to anticipate which object comes next in the pattern.

What to Do

Review the directions on each page with your child. Then have your child name the shapes on each page. Next, have your child complete the patterns on the pattern pages.

Keep On Going!

Around the home or while shopping, have your child identify the many shapes he or she sees. Then together, draw the shapes on paper. Cut them out and create different patterns.

Say the words. Color the pictures.

circle

square

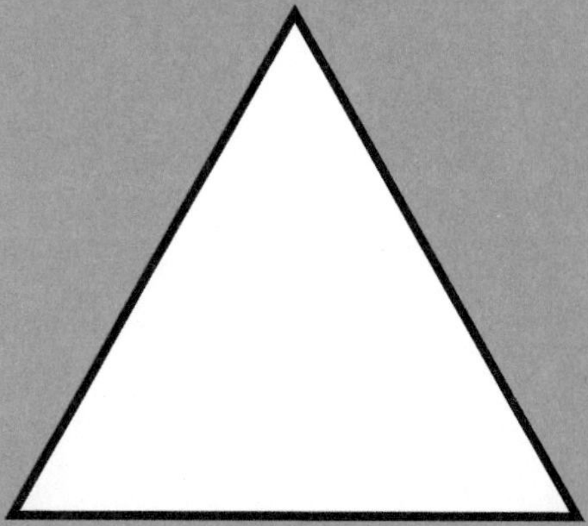

triangle

Say the words. Color the pictures.

rectangle

star

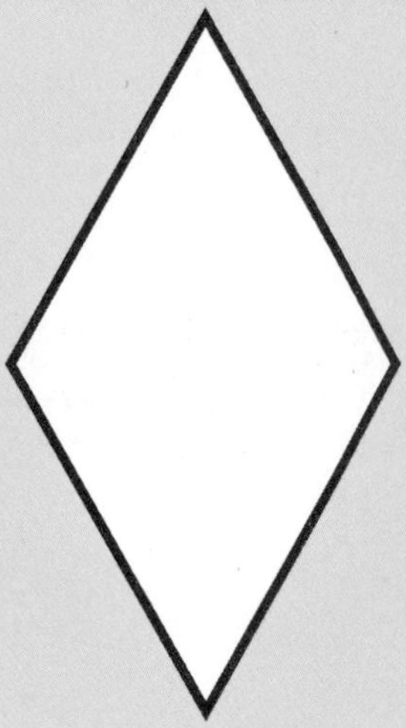

diamond

Scholastic

Say the words. Color the pictures.

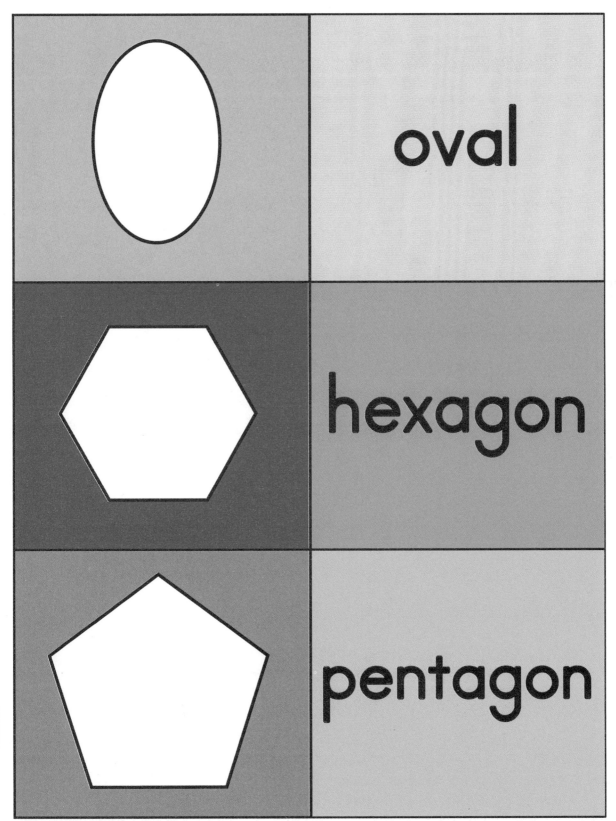

oval

hexagon

pentagon

Color the circles red. Color the squares blue.

Color the triangles orange. Color the rectangles green.

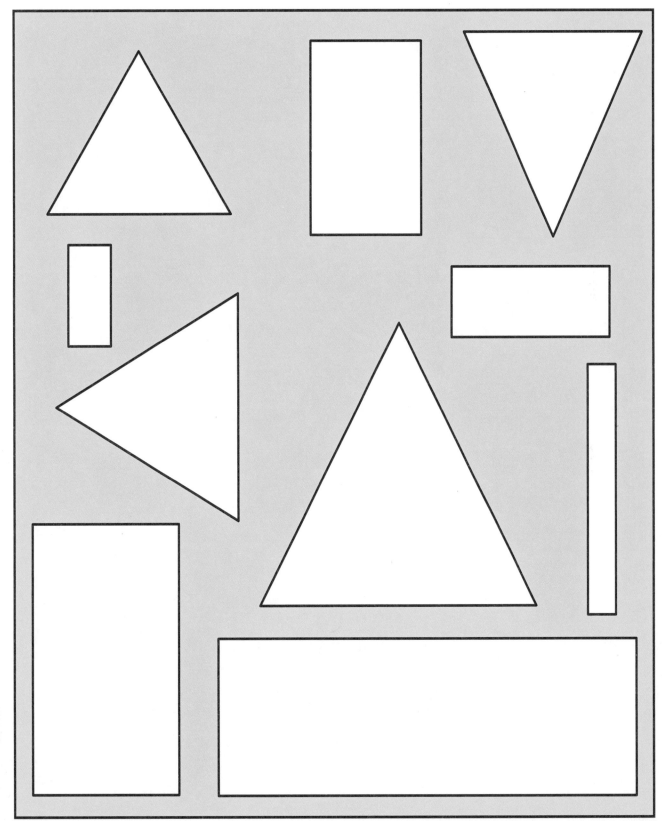

Scholastic

Color the diamonds purple. Color the ovals yellow.

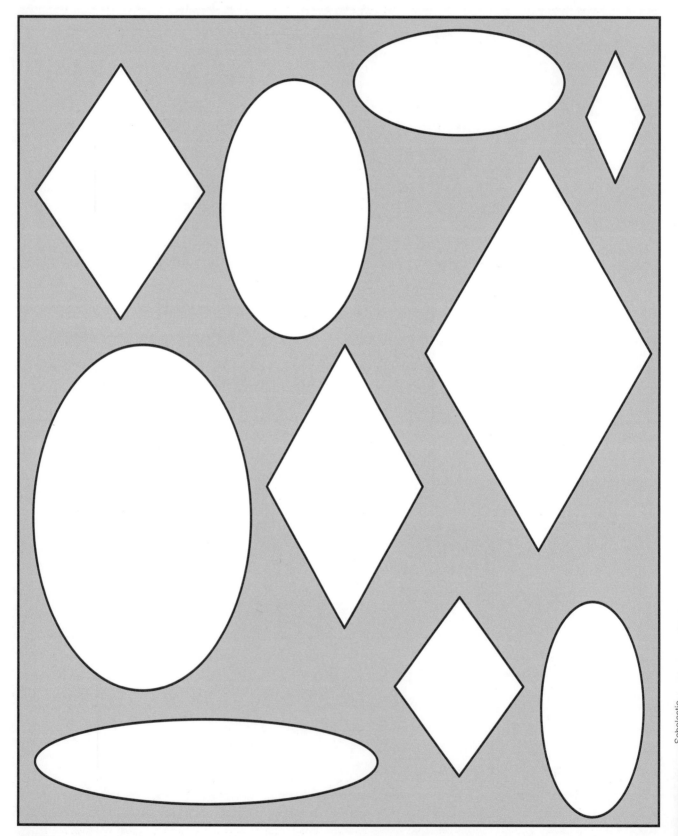

Reading & Math · Kindergarten

Color the hexagons pink. Color the pentagons brown.

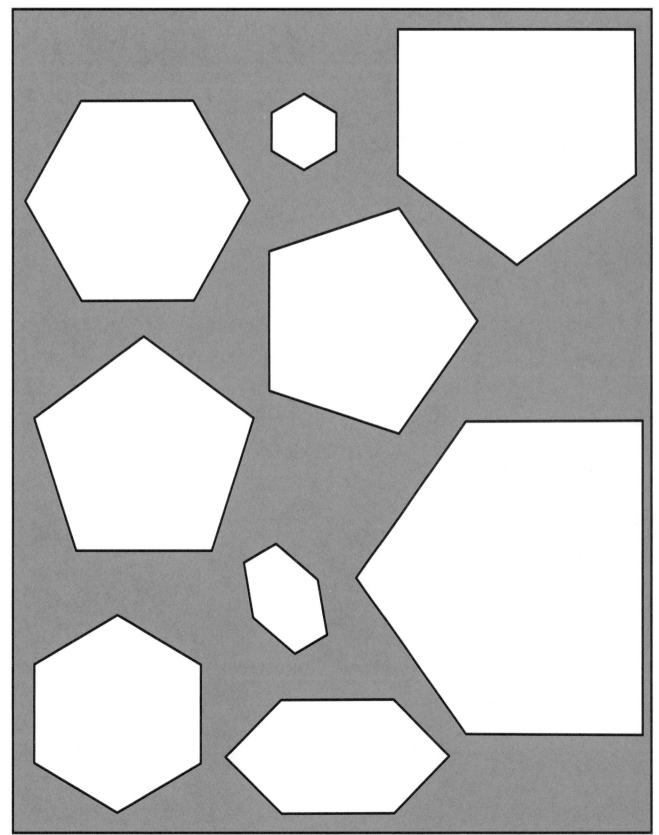

Scholastic

Color.  = black ■ = blue ▲ = red

▬ = brown ● = green ⬭ = yellow

Scholastic

Draw a line to the shape that comes next.

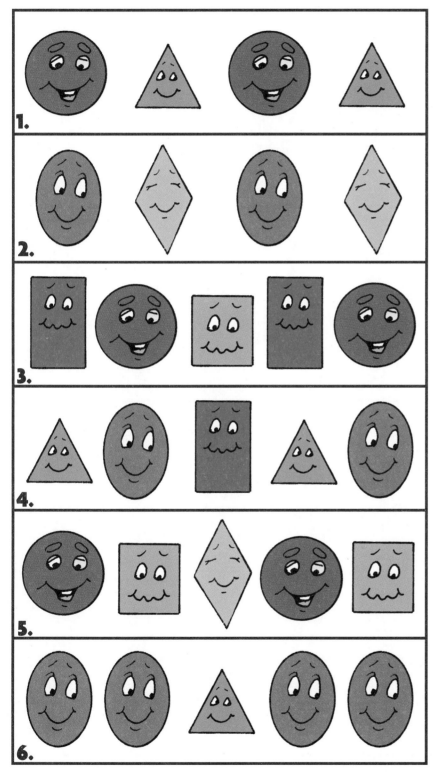

1.

2.

3.

4.

5.

6.

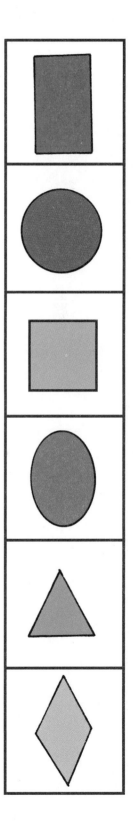

Scholastic

Draw what comes next in the box at the end of each row.

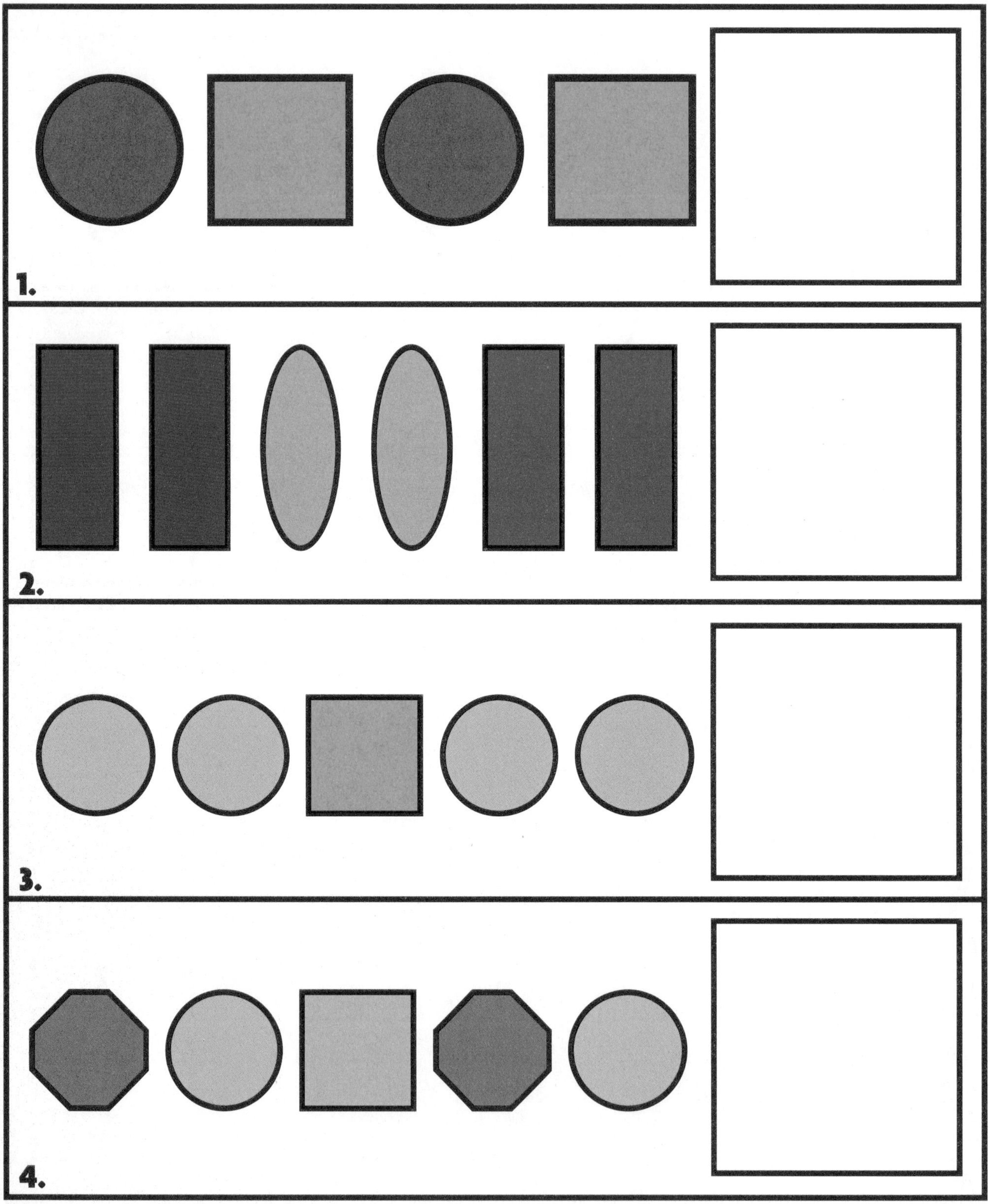

1.

2.

3.

4.

Scholastic

Draw what comes next in the box at the end of each row.

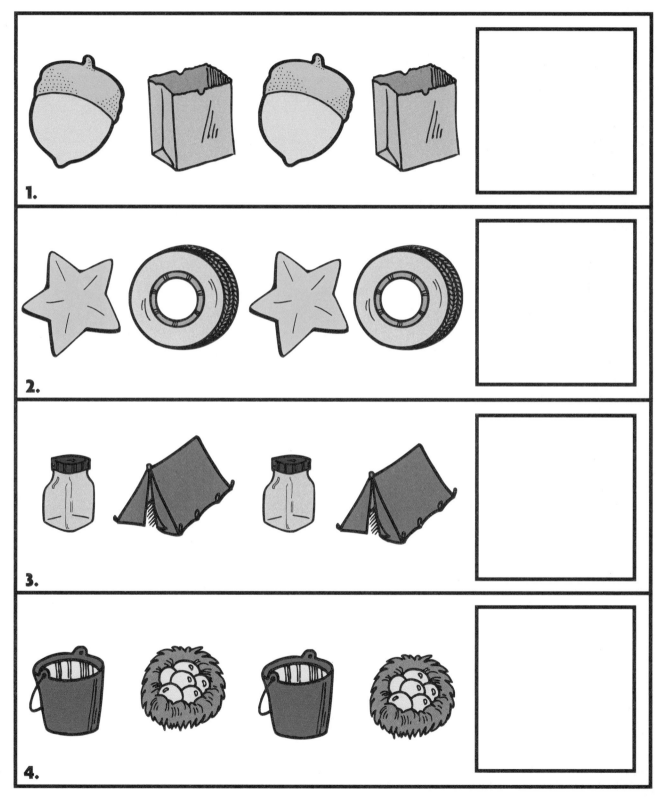

1.

2.

3.

4.

Scholastic

These vehicles are making patterns.

(1) **Look** at each pattern.

(2) **Cut** out the vehicles at the bottom of the page.

(3) **Glue** the vehicle that comes next in each row.

Scholastic

These insects are making patterns.

1 **Look** at each pattern.

2 **Cut** out the bugs at the bottom of the page.

3 **Glue** the bug that comes next in each row.

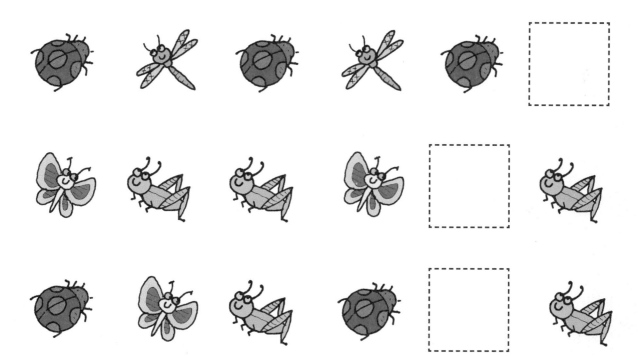

Shapes & Patterns Practice Test

Color the bubble next to the correct answer.

1. How many sides does a square have?

  ○ **A** 1

  ○ **B** 2

  ○ **C** 3

  ○ **D** 4

2. How many sides does a hexagon have?

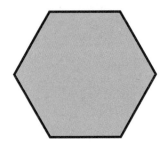

  ○ **F** 6

  ○ **G** 5

  ○ **H** 4

  ○ **J** 3

Scholastic

Shapes & Patterns Practice Test

Color the bubble next to the correct answer.

3. Which shape comes next in the pattern?

○ **A**   circle

○ **B**   hexagon

○ **C**   triangle

○ **D**   square

4. Which shape comes next in the pattern?

○ **F**   oval

○ **G**   hexagon

○ **H**   diamond

○ **J**   circle

Scholastic

Problem Solving

Have you heard the old saying, "A picture is worth a thousand words"? Pictures can sometimes explain things better than words can. In this section, your child will learn how to use pictures to solve problems.

What to Do
Read the directions on each page with your child. Have your child complete the activities. Together, review his or her work. Praise him or her for being a "super sleuth."

Keep On Going!
With your child, put together puzzles or play games that require him or her to find a way out of a maze.

Look at the picture.

Write the number.

How many?

How many in all?

1. and [ ]

2. and [ ]

3. and [ ]

4. and [ ]

5. and [ ]

6. and [ ]

Circle how many you see in the picture.

1.		1	5
2.		4	2
3.		8	5
4.		6	3
5.		7	10
6.		2	8
7.		9	7
8.		10	7
9.		3	1

Circle how many you see in all.

10.	+ =	8	9	10
11.	+ =	3	8	9
12.	+ =	6	2	4

Scholastic

Look at the picture.

Write the number.

How many?

How many in all?

1. ✈ and 🚗 ☐

2. 🚚 and ✈ ☐

3. 🚐 and 🚲 ☐

4. 🚐 and 🚁 ☐

5. 🚗 and 🚚 ☐

6. 🚁 and ✈ ☐

Scholastic

Help the bee get to his hive.

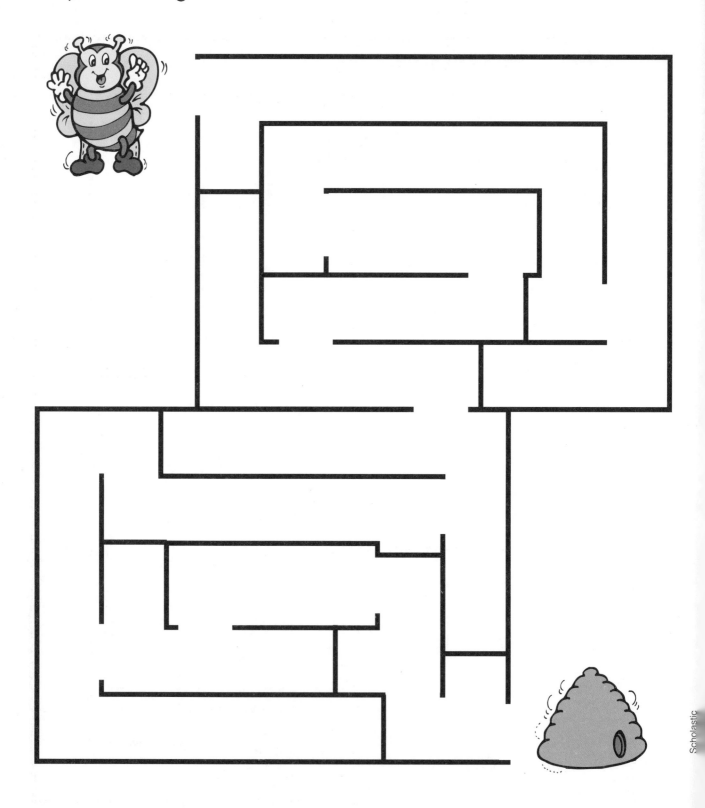

Scholastic

Help the baby ducks find the mother duck.

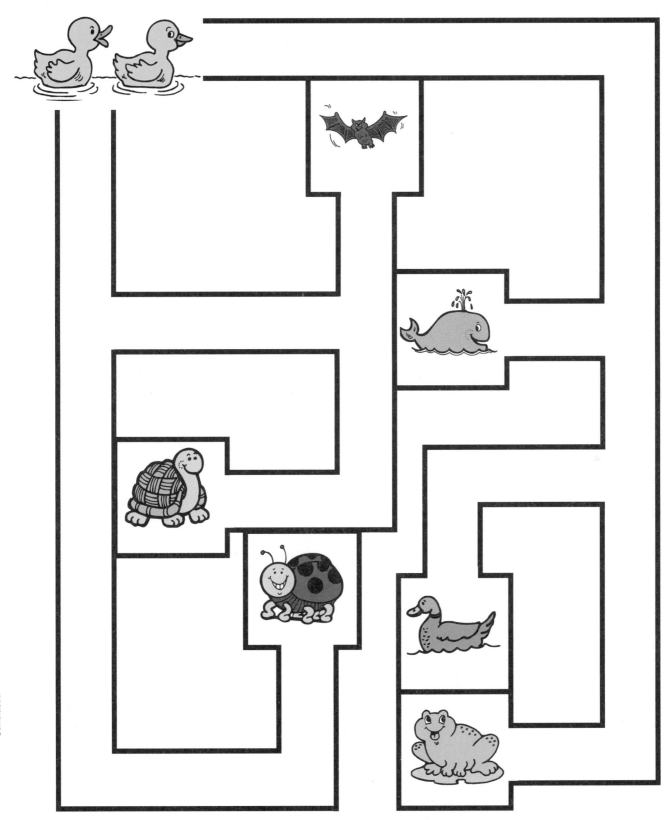

Problem Solving Practice Test

Color the bubble next to the correct answer.

Which does **not** belong?

1	P	8	6

○ **A**   1

● **B**   P

○ **C**   8

○ **D**   6

1. Which does **not** belong?

C	2	Y	X

○ **A**   C

○ **B**   2

○ **C**   Y

○ **D**   X

2. Which does **not** belong?

W	B	L	9

○ **F**   W

○ **G**   B

○ **H**   L

○ **J**   9

Problem Solving Practice Test

Color the bubble next to the correct answer.

3. How many triangles are on the butterfly?

   ○ **A**   1

   ○ **B**   2

   ○ **C**   3

   ○ **D**   4

4. How many circles are on the butterfly?

   ○ **F**   3

   ○ **G**   5

   ○ **H**   7

   ○ **J**   9

Scholastic

Word Flash Cards

The words in this section can be used to build and reinforce vocabulary development. Remember to add the additional words your child learns during the year.

What to Do
Pull the pages out of the workbook. Paste them onto cardboard or posterboard. Then cut them out. Review the words often with your child.

Keep On Going!
Encourage your child to use the cards to make simple sentences. You might also have your child group words that are opposite (up/down) and words that fit into the same category (for example, food: eggs, vegetables, fruits).

book	touch
teacher	smell
bus	hear
friends	taste
school	fall
leaves	pick
apples	farmer
see	boots

car	bread
truck	milk
van	fruit
airplane	vegetables
rain	dog
clouds	cat
sun	gerbil
snow	bfish

rabbit	make
and	me
big	my
can	play
I	come
in	down
is	for
it	here

run	are
blocks	at
the	came
to	did
up	eat
we	have
you	like
am	no

on	who
out	by
ran	above
she	below
they	behind
under	ahead
want	sled
what	ball

Get Ready for
Grade 1

In this section of the workbook, your child will get a preview of the new skills he or she will learn in Grade 1. The activity pages in this section were chosen to help your child develop the skills necessary to be successful. Here are some of the skills and concepts covered:

• Writing the days of the week and the months of the year

• Identifying words with silent consonants

• Understanding the relationship between letters and the sounds they make

• Identifying words with long and short vowels

• Understanding the reading process

• Understanding some basic reading readiness skills such as finding the main idea, drawing conclusions, and cause and effect

• Understanding the concept of synonyms

• Identifying compound words

• Understanding and using key mechanics of writing: capitalization and punctuation

• Understanding concepts related to addition and subtraction

• Understanding concepts related to time and money

• Identifying, writing, and grouping numbers from 1–20

• Identifying shapes such as circles, squares, rectangles, triangles, hexagons, and pentagons

• Identifying and extending patterns

• Solving problems using pictures

Days of the Week

Trace and write.

Sunday

Monday

Tuesday

Wednesday

Thursday

Friday

Saturday

 Reading & Math • Kindergarten

Months of the Year

Jan.   Feb.   March   April   May   June

Trace and write.

January

February

March

April

May

June

Scholastic

Months of the Year

Trace and write.

July

August

September

October

November

December

Scholastic

Say each picture name and listen to the beginning sound.
Find the picture at the bottom of the page that has the same
beginning sound. Write the letter of the matching picture in
the heart.

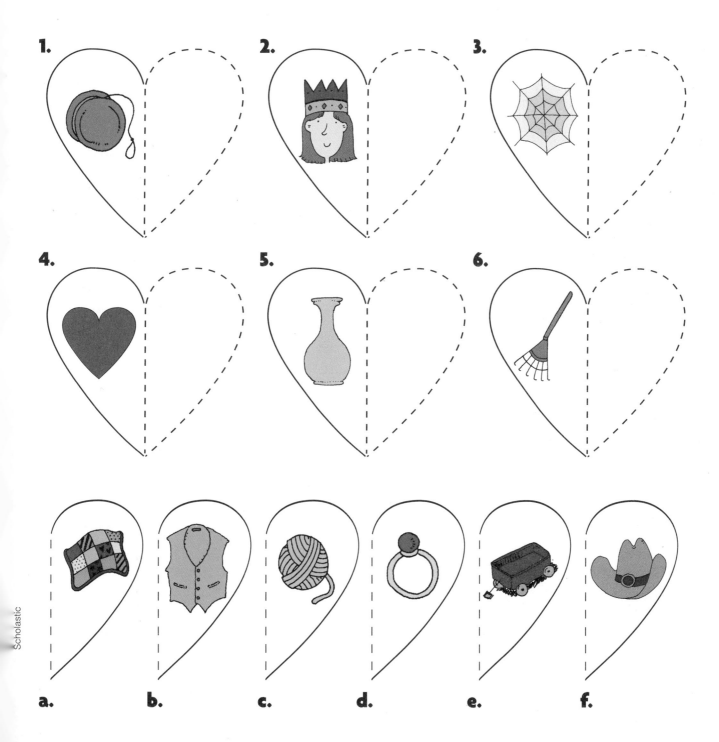

1.

2.

3.

4.

5.

6.

a.

b.

c.

d.

e.

f.

K *makes the sound you hear at the beginning of the words* **Katie** *and* **kangaroo**.

Find and circle the pictures that begin with **k**.

X *makes the sound of* **ks**. *(Hint: Say the word* **kiss** *very fast!) Most of the time, an* **x** *is in the middle or at the end of a word.*

Help Superhero X put the missing **x** in each word. Then draw a line to the matching picture.

fo___

mi___er

ta___i

e___it

a___

si___

o___

bo___

e___ercise

tu___edo

Scholastic

*Sometimes a consonant may make no sound at all. For example, when **k** and **n** come together, the **k** is silent. When **w** and **r** come together, the **w** is silent. When **r** and **h** come together, the **h** is silent.*

Look at the words and pictures. Make a sleepy eye, like this, above the consonant that is silent. Do not color it. Then color the other letters in the word.

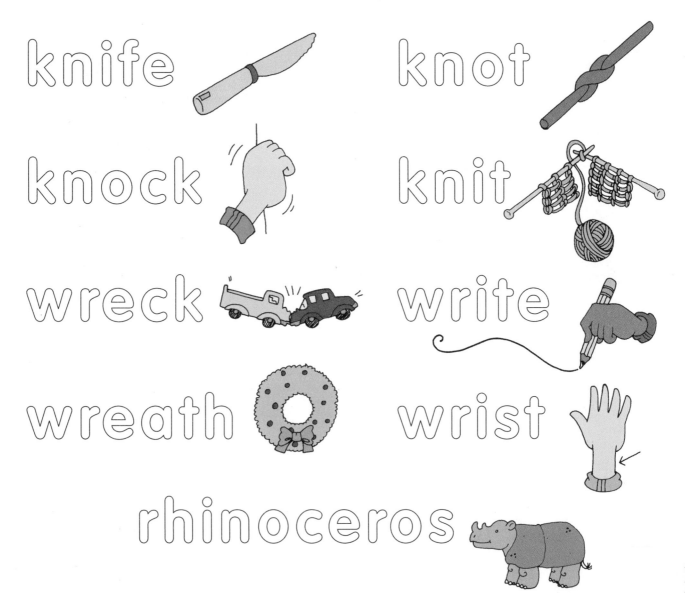

knife

knot

knock

knit

wreck

write

wreath

wrist

rhinoceros

Make your own rhyming words. Look at the picture and say the word. Copy the word. Then change the first letter using each of the letters on the hammer to make new words.

h c m t w f

p s r m f h b

f j l h

s l b

ball

cat

dog

hand

📖 Use a list word to complete each sentence.

List Words: | at | had | an | can | as | and |

1. We went to _____ apple farm.

2. We picked green _____ red apples.

3. One apple was as big _____ a ball.

4. We _____ lots of fun!

5. We went home _____ dinnertime.

6. Now Mom _____ make apple pie.

 Each list word is hidden two times. Circle the words.

hidanaastcan

kuhadtatiand

ashadinande

dahcaniatean

🏆 Write the challenge word that matches each clue.

lamp   fast

I can be turned off and on. I am a _____.

I am not slow. I am _____.

 The **short-u sound** *is the beginning sound of the word* **umbrella**.

A. Read each list word. Circle the letter that makes the short-*u* sound.

 Read.

 Copy.

 Organize.

1. up

2. but

3. run

4. bug

5. mud

6. jump

1. _____

2. _____

3. _____

4. _____

5. _____

6. _____

two-letter list word

_____

three-letter list words

_____

_____

_____

_____

 Challenge Words

7. funny

8. puppy

7. _____

8. _____

four-letter list word

_____

B. Write the list word that rhymes with each word.

1. bud _____   2. lump _____   3. hut _____

4. sun _____   5. tug _____   6. cup _____

Scholastic

Reading & Math · Kindergarten 295

 The **long-**e **sound** *can also be spelled with the letter* e *like in the word* **he** *and the letters* ee *like in the word* **need**.

A. Read each list word. Circle the letters that make the long-*e* sound.

Read.	Copy.	Organize.
1. me	1. _____	list words with long-*e* sound spelled *ee*
2. tree	2. _____	
3. we	3. _____	_____
4. need	4. _____	_____
5. see	5. _____	_____
6. feet	6. _____	_____

🏆 **Challenge Words**

list words with long-*e* sound spelled *e*

7. sleep	7. _____	_____
8. sheep	8. _____	_____

B. Write the list word that begins with the same sound as each picture.

1.  _____   2.  _____   3.  _____

4. _____   5. _____   6.  _____

Scholastic

The **long-**i **sound** *can be spelled with the letters* i_e *like in the word* **ice** *and the letter* y *like in the word* **try***.*

A. Read each list word. Circle the letter that makes the long-*i* sound.

Read.

1. by

2. like

3. I

4. my

5. kite

6. fly

Challenge Words

7. time

8. hi

Copy.

1. _____

2. _____

3. _____

4. _____

5. _____

6. _____

7. _____

8. _____

Organize.

list words with *i_e*

_____

_____

list words with *y*

_____

_____

_____

the shortest list word

_____

B. Write the list word that rhymes with each picture.

1. _____

2. _____

C. Write four list words that rhyme with each other.

_____   _____   _____   _____

Scholastic

The letters th *make the sound at the beginning of the word* **thorn**.

A. Read each list word. Circle the letters *th* in each word.

📕 **Read.**

✏️ **Copy.**

🔤 **Organize.**

1. the
2. this
3. with
4. then
5. bath
6. that

list words that begin with *th*

_____

_____

_____

_____

1. _____
2. _____
3. _____
4. _____
5. _____
6. _____

🏆 **Challenge Words**

7. them
8. they

7. _____
8. _____

list words that end with *th*

_____

_____

B. 🎧 Write the list word that rhymes with each word.

1. math _____   2. den _____   3. rat _____

👀 Unscramble each list word.

4. het _____   5. hiwt _____   6. tsih _____

*The letters or make the sound at the beginning of the word **ornament**.*

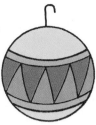

A. Read each list word. Circle the letters *or* in each word.

 Read.

 Copy.

 Organize.

1. or

2. corn

3. porch

4. horn

5. for

6. short

 Challenge Words

7. your

8. horse

1. _____

2. _____

3. _____

4. _____

5. _____

6. _____

7. _____

8. _____

two- or three-letter list words

_____

_____

four- or five-letter list words

_____

_____

_____

_____

B. Write the list word that begins with the same sound as each picture.

1.  _____

2. _____

3. _____

4. _____

5. _____

6. _____

Scholastic

Tim is a good reader.
He uses clues to help him read.
First, he looks at the pictures.
That helps him know what the
story is about. Next, he reads the
title of the story. Now he knows a
little more. As he reads the story,
the words make pictures in his mind.

Color in the book beside the correct answer.

1. Who is Tim?

 a good reader   math whiz

2. What does Tim do first?

 reads the story   looks at the pictures

3. What else helps Tim know what the story will be about?

 the title   the page number

4. As he reads, what makes pictures in Tim's mind?

 the letters   the words

Scholastic

Details *are parts of a story. Details help you understand what the story is about.*

Ricky loved to go camping. One day during reading class, he began to daydream about camping in the mountains. He thought about going fishing and riding horses. It would be fun to gather logs to build a campfire and cook hot dogs. He and his dad could set up the tent near some big trees. He wished he were in his canoe right now. Just then, Ricky heard his teacher say, "Ricky, it is your turn to read." Oh no! He had lost the place!

Circle these things from the story hidden in the picture below: a fish, a fishing pole, a log for the campfire, a hot dog, a tree, and a canoe.

1. Where was Ricky during this story?_____

_____

2. Where would Ricky like to have been? _____

_____

*The **main idea** tells what the whole story is about.*

Today I went to the circus. My favorite part of the circus was the clowns. Clowns can do funny tricks. A clown named Pinky turned flips on the back of a horse. Fancy Pants juggled balls while he was singing a funny song. Happy Hal made balloons into animal shapes. Then twelve clowns squeezed into a tiny car and rode away.

Color in the ball that tells the main idea.

Pinky rides a horse.

Balloons can be shaped like animals.

Clowns can do funny tricks.

Clowns drive tiny cars.

Fancy Pants sang a song.

*When you use your own thoughts to answer the question, "How could that have happened?" you are **drawing conclusions**.*

I bought a fancy rug today. It was made of brightly colored yarn. I placed it on the floor in front of the TV and sat on it. All of a sudden, it lifted me up in the air! The rug and I flew around the house. Then out the door we went. High above the trees, we soared like an eagle. Finally, the rug took me home, and we landed in my backyard.

How could that have happened? To find out, use your crayons to trace over each line. Use a different color on each line. Write the letter from that line in the box at the bottom of the rug.

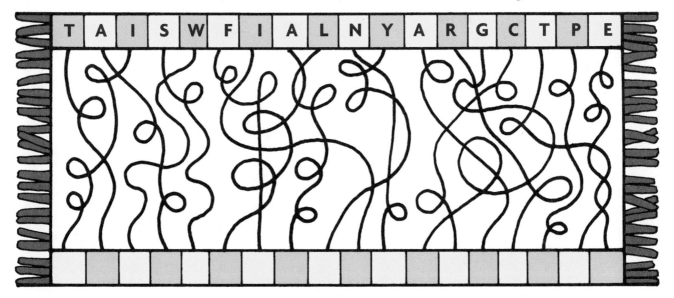

T A I S W F I A L N Y A R G C T P E

Could this story really happen? Draw a rug around your answer.

Yes   **No**

*In a story, there is usually a reason something happens. This is the **cause**. What happens as a result is the **effect**.*

Sandy went on a vacation in the mountains with her parents and little brother Austin. They were staying in a small cabin without any electricity or running water. It was fun to have lanterns at night and to bathe in the cold mountain stream. The biggest problem for Sandy was she missed her best friend, Kendra. Sandy found her dad's cell phone and called Kendra. They talked for nearly an hour! When Sandy's dad went to call his office, the cell phone was dead. He was NOT a happy camper!

Draw a line to match the first part of each sentence to the second part that makes it true.

1. Sandy used lanterns at night because

2. Sandy bathed in a stream because

3. Sandy felt better about missing Kendra because

4. Sandy's dad could not call his office because

she talked to her on the cell phone.

the cabin had no running water.

the cabin had no electricity.

the cell phone was dead.

Write about something you did that caused a huge "effect."

Read the story then answer the questions.

If I Were King

I would like to be a king. I would wear a robe with fur on it. I would wear a gold crown on my head. I would call the land I rule "Funville." Every year we would have a parade. I would want all of the people in Funville to be happy.

1. What would I like to be?

2. What would be on my robe?

3. What would I wear on my head?

4. What would I call my land?

5. What would happen every year in Funville?

6. Do I want the people in Funville to be happy?

Synonyms *are words with the same or nearly the same meanings.*

Read each word at the top of the box. Circle every other letter. Write the letters in order on the line to spell a synonym. The first one is done for you.

1. begin

start

2. glad

_____

3. loud
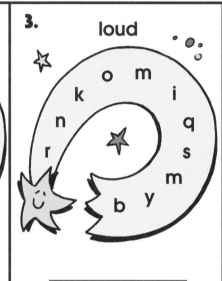

_____

4. little

_____

5. see

_____

6. big

_____

Compound words *are two words joined together to make one new word.*

Draw a line to connect the boxes to make compound words.
Write the compound word.

	door
	foot
	sun
	cup
	bee
	bed
	flower
	dog
	pop
	tooth
	book

	hive
	flower
	time
	bell
	brush
	ball
	shelf
	cake
	corn
	pot
	house

_____

_____

_____

_____

_____

_____

_____

_____

_____

Use a word from the box to describe the character trait shown in each picture.

polite	cooperative	helpful	honest	responsible	kind

1. _____

2. _____

3. _____

4. _____

5. _____

6. _____

*A sentence always begins with a **capital letter**.*

Copy each sentence correctly on the line.

1 the cat sat.

_____

- -

_____

2 the dog sat.

_____

- -

_____

3 i see the cat.

_____

- -

_____

4 i can see.

_____

- -

_____

*A telling sentence ends with a **period**.*

Write a period where it belongs in each sentence.
Read the sentences to a friend.

1 Dan is in the cab

2 The cat is in the cab

3 Mom is in the cab

4 We see Dan and Mom

Read the words. Write each word at the end of the correct sentence.

van.   red.

5 We can go in the _____

6 The van is _____

Words that compare two people, places or things end in -er.

Read each sentence. Circle the word that compares. Then draw a line under the two words that name the two things that are being compared.

1. Beth is older than Carmen.

2. The tree is taller than the bush.

3. The plant is smaller than the ants.

4. The fly is faster than the ants.

Read each word. Then write the comparing word.

5. tall _____

6. old _____

7. slow _____

8. bold _____

Add.

1. 3
   + 0

2. 2
   + 3

3. 0
   + 2

4. 6
   + 0

5. 1
   + 2

6. 4
   + 0

7. 1
   + 5

8. 3
   + 0

9. 4
   + 2

10. 5
    + 0

11. 3
    + 1

12. 0
    + 6

13. 2
    + 1

14. 3
    + 3

15. 4
    + 1

16. 1
    + 1

17. 2
    + 2

18. 5
    + 1

19. 0
    + 0

20. 3
    + 2

Subtract.

Subtract!

1. $6 - 2 =$ 2. $3 - 1 =$ 3. $2 - 0 =$

4. $5 - 1 =$ 5. $6 - 2 =$ 6. $5 - 5 =$

7. $3 - 2 =$ 8. $6 - 3 =$ 9. $5 - 2 =$

10. $3 - 0 =$ 11. $1 - 1 =$ 12. $5 - 0 =$

13. $4 - 4 =$ 14. $5 - 4 =$ 15. $6 - 3 =$ 16. $4 - 3 =$

17. $6 - 0 =$ 18. $4 - 1 =$ 19. $2 - 0 =$ 20. $5 - 2 =$

Read the problem. Write the correct time under each clock.
Then answer the question.

_____ : _____   _____ : _____   _____ : _____

1. The hands on my clock are in a straight line.

Both hands on my clock point to the same number.

What time does my clock show?

_____

_____ : _____   _____ : _____   _____ : _____

2. The hands on my clock do **not** show 12:00.

The hands on my clock do **not** show 10:00.

What time does my clock show?

_____

Read the problem then answer the question.

| 25¢ | 10¢ | 5¢ | 1¢ | 25¢ | 10¢ | 5¢ | 1¢ | 25¢ | 10¢ | 5¢ | 1¢ |

1. I have one coin in my pocket.

My coin is silver.

The value of my coin is 10¢.

What is the change in my pocket?

_____

| 25¢ | 10¢ | 5¢ | 1¢ | 25¢ | 10¢ | 5¢ | 1¢ | 25¢ | 10¢ | 5¢ | 1¢ |

2. I have three coins in my pocket.

I have less than 10¢.

I have less than 5¢.

What is the change in my pocket?

_____

Scholastic

Answer Key

READING/LANGUAGE ARTS

The Alphabet/Manuscript Handwriting

Page 14–63
Review letter formation, spelling, and drawing/coloring on each page.

Page 64–67
1. E   2. O   3. Y   4. L
5. h   6. q   7. I   8. v

Phonics

Page 69
21 consonants; Color: F, M, B, J, X, L

Page 70
bird, ball, belt, boat, banana, basket, bell, books, boots, bat EXTRA: bee

Page 71
domino, dog, dollar, duck, dice, deer, dinosaur, door EXTRA: dentist

Page 72
fox, five, fish, fork, fan, feather, football, four EXTRA: firefighter

Page 73
lamp, lace, leaf, ladder, ladybug, lake, lamb, leg, lightning, lemon, letter, lettuce, lips, lizard, lobster, log
EXTRA: love

Page 74
motorcycle, milk, mop, mirror, mouse, mitten, monkey, moon, money
EXTRA: mother

Page 75
nose, nine, needle, nail, nuts, net, necklace EXTRA: newspaper

Page 76
popcorn, pineapple, porcupine, penguin, police officer, paste, puppet, pencil, paper EXTRA: penny

Page 77
rest, run, ride, rock, rake, roll, read, rope, rip, row, race, rush
EXTRA: rocket

Page 78
saw, six, sun, school bus, sink, soap, starfish, seal EXTRA: sandwich

Page 79
tiger, turtle, teapot, toast, telephone, television, table, tape EXTRA: tent

Page 80
Willy, worm, wanted, watermelon, window, wagon, wiggled, wall, wow, was, wonderful EXTRA: wind

Page 81
1. k, s, k, s   2. k, s, s, k
3. k, s, k, k   4. s, k, s, k

Page 82
1. g, g, j, g   2. j, g, g, j
3. g, g, j, j

Page 83
bear-r   dog-g   cat-t   deer-r
raccoon-n lamb-m lion-n camel-l
goat-t
EXTRA: octopus

Page 84
1. n, l, r   2. n, m, k
3. d, x, g   4. r, l, f
EXTRA: dream

Page 85
1. rug, flag, g   2. spoon, sun, n
3. chair, star, r   4. broom, gum, m
5. hat, foot, t   6. ball, bell, l
7. cup, mop, p

Page 86
orange: dress, mouse
purple: ball, bell, shell
green: map, rope, lamp

Page 87
1. pot, pumpkin   2. nest, nine
3. queen, quarter 4. duck, dog
5. fox, farmer   6. flag, pig
7. bike, cake   8. bus, dress
9. hat, goat   10. ball, bell

Page 88
Review that directions have been followed.

Page 89
1. r<u>a</u>t   2. h<u>a</u>t
3. t<u>a</u>ck   4. m<u>a</u>sk
5. f<u>a</u>n   6. l<u>a</u>mp
7. c<u>a</u>p   8. D<u>a</u>d
9. tr<u>a</u>p   10. h<u>a</u>nd
11. cl<u>a</u>p   12. bl<u>a</u>ck

Page 90
leg, net, belt, desk, neck, ten, nest, sled EXTRA: yes

Page 91
chick, igloo inn, pig, fish, bib, chin, ship, pin, six

Page 92
green: mop, hot, hop, log, sock, dog, frog, clock

Page 93
rug, drum, gum, tub, but, rut, dust, bug, sub, club, mug, mud, cub, cup, slug, dug, hug, sun, plug, jug, nut, must, duck, truck

Page 94
hat, mat, bat, cat
EXTRA: possible answers: sat, pat, fat, vat

Page 95
dad, mad, sad, glad

Page 96
man, fan, pan, can

Page 97
1. pan   2. cat   3. mad   4. van

Scholastic

Page 98
ten, hen, pen, men

Page 99
red, bed, sled

Page 100
jet, pet, net, wet, vet

Page 101
wing, sing, ring, string

Page 102–103
Review that directions have been followed.

Page 104
mop, hop, stop, top

Page 105
Review that directions have been followed.

Page 106
run, bun, sun

Page 107
1. gate, late, skate
2. fail, pail, tail
3. save, wave, brave
4. gain, stain, train

Page 108
wheel, feet, meat, teeth, peach, queen, sheep, key
EXTRA: eraser

Page 109
ride: hide, side, tide, wide, glide, pride
mice: nice, rice, price, slice, spice, twice
fine: dine, line, mine, vine, shine, spine
dime: lime, time, chime, grime, prime, slime
night: light, might, sight, tight, flight, bright
bike: hike, like, pike, spike, trike, strike

Page 110
Review that directions have been followed.
EXTRA: toad

Page 111
1. fruit, rude, duke
2. cube, flute, clue
3. rule, June, true
EXTRA: blue

Page 112
Review that directions have been followed.

Page 113
Review that words and pictures match.
EXTRA: blood

Page 114
1. bread   2. brain
3. bracelet   4. bride
5. bricks   6. bridge
7. broom   8. brush
EXTRA: bruise

Page 115
orange: clam, clap, clock, claws, climb, clothes, clouds, clover
EXTRA: closet

Page 116
5, 1, 4, 6, 2, 3

Page 117
drain, drive, dragonfly, dress, drop, drum, drill, drink, dryer

Page 118
sneaker, snow, snowman, snorkel, snap, snail, sneeze, snout

Page 119
spear, spoon, sponge, spinner, spur, spill, spaghetti, spaceship
EXTRA: spinach

Page 120–123
1. c   2. a   3. B   4. J
5. C   6. G   7. A   8. G

Following Directions
Page 125–130
Review that directions have been followed.

Page 131–132
1. C   2. G   3. A   4. G

Word Building
Page 134–168
Review that directions have been followed; review writing.

Page 169
1. boots   2. sled   3. mittens
4. snow   5. coat

Page 170
1. truck   2. ball
3. puzzle   4. doll
5. blocks   5. bat

Page 171
1. socks   2. coat
3. sweater   3. shirt
4. pants

Page 172
1. candles   2. gifts
3. cake   4. hats
5. balloons

Page 173
1. birds   2. flowers
3. basket   3. bee
4. egg

Page 174
1. slug   2. ant
3. butterfly 4. ladybug
5. bee

Page 175
1. flower   2. leaves
3. roots   4. pots
5. seeds

Page 176
1. ball   2. tiger
3. sun   4. nest
5. queen   6. duck

Page 177–179
Review that directions have been followed.

Page 180–183
1. B   2. H   3. B   4. F
5. D   6. H   7. B   8. G

Reading Readiness
Page 185
Review that directions have been followed.

Page 186
3, 1, 2; review writing.

Page 187
1, 3, 2; review writing.

Page 188
4, 1, 2, 3; review writing.

Page 189
Muddy mat should be checked; review writing.

Page 190
Nest with baby birds should be checked; review writing.

Page 191
3, 2, 1

Page 192
3, 1, 2

Page 193–194
Review that directions have been followed.

Page 195
Girl on ladder should be checked; review writing.

Page 196
Bread and peanut butter should be checked; review writing.

Page 197
1. fish   2. trucks
3. clothes

Page 198
1. glasses   2. fruit
3. pens   4. tools

Page 199
blue: 1, 3, 7   orange: 2, 4, 5, 6, 8

Page 200
1, 2, 3, 4, 6, 8

Page 201–204
1. C   2. G   3. C   4. H
5. C   6. F   7. D   8. G

Thinking Skills
Page 206
1. train   2. anchor
3. zebra   4. stapler
5. eggs

Page 207
1. guitar   2. paintbrush
3. stethoscope   4. knight
5. clown

Page 208
1. bulb   2. potato
3. rope   4. pig

Page 209
globe, ball, marble

Page 210–211
1. A   2. J   3. B   4. F

MATHEMATICS
Numbers & Number Concepts
Page 213–234
Review that directions have been followed and numbers/letters are formed correctly.

Page 235
Review that directions have been followed.

Page 236–245
Review that directions have been followed.

Page 246–249
1. C   2. H   3. D   4. H
5. B   6. F   7. D   8. H

Shapes & Patterns
Page 251–258
Review that directions have been followed.

Page 259
1. circle   2. oval
3. square   4. rectangle
5. diamond   6. triangle

Page 260
1. circle   2. oval
3. square   4. square

Page 261
1. acorn   2. star   3. jar   4. pail

Page 262–263
Review that directions have been followed.

Page 264–265
1. D   2. F   3. B   4. F

Problem Solving
Page 267
3 ants, 5 flies, 4 bees, 2 butterflies, 1 ladybug, 2 grasshoppers
1. 7   2. 6   3. 6   4. 4
5. 5   6. 9

Page 268
1. 1   2. 4   3. 5   4. 3
5. 10   6. 2   7. 9   8. 7
9. 3   10. 10   11. 8   12. 6

Page 269
3 planes, 4 trucks, 5 vans, 5 cars, 2 helicopters, 1 bicycle
1. 8   2. 7   3. 6   4. 7
5. 9   6. 5

Page 270–271
Review that directions have been followed.

Page 272–273
1. B   2. J   3. D   4. H

GET READY FOR GRADE 1
Page 286–288
Review letter formation and spelling.

Page 289
1. c   2. a   3. e   4. f
5. b   6. d

Page 290
kitten, kiss, key, kick, kite, king, kangaroo

Page 291–292
Review that directions have been followed.

Page 293
hand: sand, land, band
ball: hall, call, mall, tall, wall, fall
dog: fog, jog, log, hog
cat: pat, sat, rat, mat, fat, hat, bat

Page 294
1. an   2. and   3. as   4. had
5. at   6. can   EXTRA: lamp, fast

Page 295
A. Review that directions have been followed; two-letter word: up; three-letter words: but, run, bug, mud; four-letter word: jump
B. 1. mud   2. jump
   3. but   4. run
   5. bug   6. up

Page 296
A. Review that directions have been followed; long *ee* words: see, tree, feet, need; long *e* words: me, we
B. 1. see 2. tree 3. we 4. feet
5. me   6. need

Page 297
A. Review that directions have been followed; i_e words: like, kite; y words: by, my, fly; shortest word: I
B. 1. like   2. night
C. by, I, my, fly

Page 298
A. Review that directions have been followed; begin with *th* words: the, this, then, that; words that end with *th*: with, bath
B. 1. bath 2. then 3. that 4. the
5. with 6. this

Page 299
A. Review that directions have been followed; 2- or 3-letter words: or, for; 4- or 5-letter words: corn, porch, horn, short
B. 1. short 2. porch 3. corn 4. horn
5. or 6. for

Page 300
1. a good reader
2. looks at the pictures
3. the title
4. the words

Page 301
1. reading class
2. camping in the mountains

Page 302
Clowns can do funny tricks.

Page 303
It was a flying carpet; No.

Page 304
1. the cabin had no electricity.
2. the cabin had no running water.
3. she talked to her on the cell phone.
4. the cell phone was dead.

Page 305
1. a king   2. fur
3. gold crown   4. Funville
5. a parade   6. yes

Page 306
1. start   2. happy
3. noisy   4. small
5. look   6. large

Page 307
doorbell, football, sunflower, cupcake, beehive, bedtime, flowerpot, doghouse, popcorn, toothbrush, bookshelf

Page 308
1. responsible   2. honest
3. helpful   4. cooperative
5. kind   6. polite

Page 309
Review that directions have been followed.

Page 310
1–4. Review that periods have been added.
5. van.   6. red.

Page 311
1. older; Beth, Carmen
2. taller; tree, bush
3. smaller; plant, ants
4. faster; fly, ants
5. taller
6. older
7. slower
8. bolder

Page 312
1. 3	2. 5	3. 2	4. 6
5. 3	6. 4	7. 6	8. 3
9. 6	10. 5	11. 4	12. 6
13. 3	14. 6	15. 5	16. 2
17. 4	18. 6	19. 0	20. 5

Page 313
1. 4	2. 2	3. 2	4. 4
5. 4	6. 0	7. 1	8. 3
9. 3	10. 3	11. 0	12. 5
13. 0	14. 1	15. 3	16. 1
17. 6	18. 3	19. 2	20. 3

Page 314
1. (12:00, 6:00, 7:00) 12:00
2. (10:00, 11:00, 12:00) 11:00

Page 315
1. one dime   2. three pennies

Success with Reading & Math!

You're a Scholastic Superstar!

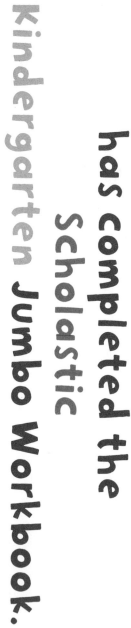

has **completed** the
Scholastic
Kindergarten Jumbo Workbook.

Presented on

Congratulations!